*Forty-inch Refracting Telescope of the Yerkes
Observatory.*

SIMON NEWCOMB'S
ASTRONOMY FOR EVERYBODY

REVISED BY

ROBERT H. BAKER, Ph.D.

Professor of Astronomy in the
University of Illinois

GARDEN CITY PUBLISHING COMPANY, INC.

GARDEN CITY, NEW YORK

A NOTE ON THE AUTHOR

EVER since its first appearance, *Astronomy for Everybody* has been one of the most popular of scientific books, well over fifty thousand copies having been sold in the United States alone. It was also published in England and was translated into many foreign languages.

Its author, Professor Simon Newcomb, was born March 10, 1835, in Nova Scotia, and died July 11, 1909, in Washington, D. C. Descended from early settlers of the colonies from Massachusetts to Maryland, he was the oldest child of a country-school teacher and earned his own living from childhood. After settling in the United States and teaching for a few years, he had so far educated himself that he became a mathematical computer and a student at the Lawrence Scientific School of Harvard, where he graduated as Bachelor of Science in 1858. The first work to win him international reputation was accomplished while he was a graduate student, aged twenty-four. This was the computation of orbits of asteroids, which resulted in proving the impossibility of the suggestions which astronomers had put forth to explain their origin. (See chapter on "The Group of Minor Planets.")

In 1861, President Lincoln commissioned him as Professor of Mathematics in the U. S. Navy. This position he held for the rest of his life, with a relative rank which rose to that of rear admiral. He was always stationed in Washington, where for sixteen years he carried on astronomical observations at the Naval

Observatory while pursuing his chosen mathematical labors. In 1877, his work as an observer ended with his assignment to duty as superintendent of the American Ephemeris and Nautical Almanac office. The volumes issued annually by this office contain tables of the principal heavenly bodies, elements, and other data of eclipses, and further matter of value to astronomers and necessary for the navigation of ships at sea. Four other governments issue similar volumes, and there was such an injurious diversity in the fundamental elements and constants of astronomy then in use that Prof. Newcomb now undertook a revision of the whole subject and the calculation of new tables of the celestial motions. Such routine parts of the work as could be assigned to assistants were carried on by naval officers and computers.

Of this enormous work, which was greater in extent than had ever before been undertaken by any one astronomer, the Encyclopædia Britannica says: "The formation of the tables of a planet has been described by Cayley [the greatest contemporary English mathematician] as 'the culminating achievement of astronomy,' but the gigantic task which Newcomb laid out for himself, and which he carried on for more than twenty years, was the building up, on an absolutely homogeneous basis, of the theory and tables of the whole planetary system." The results of this work have been adopted by astronomers of all countries and form the basis of the exact navigation of ships and air craft to-day.

"Among Newcomb's most notable achievements are

his researches in connection with the theory of the moon's motion" to which he gave his best efforts from 1868 to his last days of life. The Britannica continues: "[Even] his first work on this abstruse subject . . . is remarkable for the boldness of its conception, and constitutes an important addition to celestial dynamics." As a basis for this, he gathered in European observatories and libraries ancient and modern records of observations of the moon "covering an extreme range in time of about 2600 years."

"In view of the wide extent and importance of his labors, the variety of subjects of which he treats, and the unity of purpose which guided him throughout, Simon Newcomb must be considered as one of the most distinguished astronomers of his time."

Professor Newcomb was never hurried, nor did he neglect his long daily walks, yet by steady application he had time for so much thinking and writing that the published list of his books and articles contain 541 titles on a wide variety of subjects, including finance (of which subject he was a master) and even some fiction. He travelled much for general culture and pleasure as well as for astronomical purposes, such as to observe eclipses and transits and to supervise construction of the great telescopes for the Naval Observatory, and for Lick Observatory in California, as also for the glass for the Imperial Russian Observatory.

For nine of the early years of Johns Hopkins University he was Professor of Mathematics and Astronomy there, going to Baltimore twice a week to lecture.

After his death there was published a many-page list of the scientific honors he had received, including seventeen honorary degrees from leading and famous universities of Europe and America, high decorations from foreign governments, medals and honorary membership in all the most important scientific societies in the world.

In a short biography of Prof. Newcomb, Prof. W. W. Campbell, noted astronomer, calls him "intellectually a giant" and says: "The commanding position in astronomical science attained by Prof. Newcomb is accurately indicated by the long list of honors conferred upon him. His work, driven by untiring energy and guided by philosophic intelligence for more than half a century, placed him at the head of his profession in America, and gave him membership in a small class of the most productive astronomers of all countries and all centuries.

Since the book's first publication there have been many important discoveries in the field of astronomy. This new edition, completely revised to include these, has been edited and brought up to date by Professor Robert H. Baker, of the University of Illinois Observatory, Urbana, Illinois. As a former pupil of Dr. Newcomb's and a distinguished astronomer in his own right, he has been uniquely fitted for the task. In its present form *Astronomy for Everybody* is the final and authoritative word on a subject which exercises a universal fascination.

THE *present work grew out of articles contributed to McClure's Magazine a few years since on the Unsolved Problems of Astronomy, Total Eclipses of the Sun, and other subjects. The interest shown in these articles suggested an exposition of the main facts of astronomy in the same style. The result of the attempt is now submitted to the courteous consideration of the reader.*

The writer who attempts to set forth the facts of astronomy without any use of technical language finds himself in the dilemma of being obliged either to convey only a very imperfect idea of the subject, or to enter upon explanations of force and motion which his reader may find tedious. In grappling with this difficulty the author has followed a middle course, trying to present the subject in such a way as to be intelligible and interesting to every reader, and entering into technical explanations only when necessary to the clear understanding of such matters as the measure of time, the changes of the seasons, the varying positions of the constellations, and the aspects of the planets. It is hoped that the reader who does not wish to master these subjects will find enough to interest him in the descriptions and illustrations of celestial scenery to which the bulk of the work is devoted.

SIMON NEWCOMB.

CONTENTS

Part I.

THE CELESTIAL MOTIONS

Part II.

THE TELESCOPE

CONTENTS

Part IV.

THE PLANETS AND THEIR SATELLITES

PART V.

COMETS AND METEORS

Part VI.

THE STARS

ILLUSTRATIONS

Part I
THE CELESTIAL MOTIONS

I

OUR STELLAR SYSTEM

LET us enter upon our subject by taking a general view of the assemblage of stars in which we live, fancying ourselves looking at it from a point without its limits. Far away, indeed, is the point we must choose. To give a conception of the distance, let us measure it by the motion of light. This agent, darting through nearly 186,300 miles in every second, would make the circuit of the earth several times between two ticks of a watch. The standpoint which we choose will probably be well situated if we take it at a distance through which light would travel in a million years. It is very likely that we should at this point find ourselves almost in utter darkness, a black and starless sky surrounding us on all sides. But, in one direction, we should see a large patch of feeble light spreading over a considerable part of the heavens like a faint cloud or the first glimmer of a dawn. Possibly there might be other such patches visible in different directions, but at present we neglect them. The one which we have mentioned, and which we call our stellar system, is that which we are to inspect. We therefore fly toward it—how fast we need not say. To reach it within a year we should have to go a million times as fast as light. As we approach, it continually spreads out over more of the black sky which it at length half covers, the region behind us being still entirely black.

Before reaching this stage we begin to see points of light glimmering here and there in the mass. As we continue our course, these points become more numerous and seem to move past us and disappear behind us in the distance, while new ones continually come into view in front, as the passengers on a railway train see landscape and houses flit by them. These are stars, which, when we get well in among them, stud the whole heavens as we see them do at night. We might pass through the whole cloud at the enormous speed we have fancied, without seeing anything but stars and, perhaps, a few great nebulous masses of foggy light scattered here and there among them.

But instead of doing this, let us select one particular star and slacken our speed to make a closer inspection of it. This one is rather a small star; but as we approach it, it seems to our eyes to grow brighter. In time it is as brilliant as Venus. Then it casts a shadow; then we can read by its light; then it begins to dazzle our eyes. It looks like a little sun. It is the Sun!

Let us get into a position which, compared with the distances we have been traveling, is right alongside of the sun, though, expressed in our ordinary measure, it may be a thousand million miles away. Now, looking down and around us, we see nine or more star-like points scattered around the sun at different distances. If we watch them long enough we shall see them all in motion around the sun, completing their circuit in times ranging from three months to as much as 250 years. They move at very different distances; the most distant is a hundred times more remote from the sun than the nearest.

These star-like bodies are the planets. By careful examination we see that they differ from the stars in being opaque bodies, shining only by light borrowed from the sun.

Let us pay one of them a visit. We select the third in order from the sun. Approaching it in a direction which we may call from above, that is to say from a direction at right angles to the line drawn from it to the sun, we see it grow larger and brighter as we get nearer. When we get very near, it has the appearance of a half-moon—one hemisphere being in darkness and the other illuminated by the sun's rays. As we approach yet nearer, the illuminated part, always growing larger to our sight, assumes a mottled appearance. Still expanding, this appearance gradually resolves itself into oceans and continents, obscured over perhaps half their surface by clouds. The surface upon which we are looking continually spreads out before us, filling more and more of the sky, until we see it to be a world. We land upon it, and here we are upon the earth.

Thus, a point which was absolutely invisible while we were flying through the celestial spaces, which became a star when we got near the sun, and an opaque globe when yet nearer, now becomes the world on which we live.

This imaginary flight makes known to us a capital fact of astronomy: The great mass of stars which stud the heavens at night are suns. To express the idea in another way, the sun is merely one of the stars. Compared with its fellows it is rather a small one, for we know of stars that emit thousands or even tens of thousands of times the light and heat of the sun. Measuring things simply by their intrinsic importance, there is nothing special to distinguish our sun from the hundreds of millions of its companions. Its importance to us and its comparative greatness in our eyes arise simply from the accident of our relation to it.

The great system of stars which we have described looks to us from the earth just as it looked to us during the latter part of our imaginary flight through it. The stars which stud our sky are the same stars which we saw on our flight. The great difference between our view of the heavens and the view from a point in the starry distances is the prominent position occupied by the sun and planets. The former is so bright that during the daytime it completely obliterates the stars. If we could cut off the sun's rays from any very wide region, we should see the stars around the sun in the daytime as well as by night. These bodies surround us in all directions, as if the earth were placed in the center of the universe, as was supposed by the ancients.

THE SOLAR SYSTEM

One class of celestial objects, the galaxies, is represented by the millions of stars the arrangement and appearance of which we have just mentioned. Another is represented by a single star which is for us the most important of all the stars, and the bodies connected with it. This collection of bodies, with the sun in its center, forms a little colony all by itself, which we call the solar system. The feature of this system which

I wish first to impress on the reader's mind is its very small dimensions when compared with the distances between the stars. All around it are spaces which are almost completely void through enormous distances. If we could fly across the whole breadth of the solar system, we should not be able to see that we were any nearer the stars in front of us, nor would the constellations look in any way different than they do from our earth. An astronomer armed with the finest instruments would be able to detect a change only by the most exact observations, and then only in the case of the nearer stars.

A conception of the respective magnitudes and distances of the heavenly bodies, which will help the reader in conceiving of our portion of the universe as it is, may be gained by looking at a little model of it. Let us imagine that, in this model of the universe, the earth on which we dwell is represented by a grain of mustard seed. On this scale the moon will then be a particle about one fourth the diameter of the grain, placed at a distance of an inch from the earth. The sun will be represented by a large apple, placed at a distance of forty feet. Other planets, ranging in size from an invisible particle to a pea, must be imagined at average distances from the sun varying from fifteen feet to a third of a mile. We must then imagine all these little objects to be slowly moving around the sun at their respective distances, in times varying from three months to 250 years. As the mustard seed performs its revolution in the course of a year we must imagine the moon to accompany it, making a revolution around it every month.

On this scale a plan of the whole solar system can be laid down in a field less than a mile square. Outside of this field we should find a tract broader than the whole continent of America without a visible object in it unless perhaps comets scattered around its border. Far beyond the limits of the American continent we should find the nearest star, which, like our sun, might be represented by an apple. At still greater distances, in every direction, would be other stars, but, in the general average, they would be separated from each other as widely as the nearest star is from the sun. A region of the little model as large as the whole earth might contain only two or three stars.

We see from this how, in a flight through the universe, like the one we have imagined, we might overlook such an insignificant little body as our earth, even if we made a careful search for it. We should be like a person flying through the Mississippi Valley, looking for a grain of mustard seed which he knew was hidden somewhere on the American continent. Even the bright shining apple representing the sun might be overlooked unless we happened to pass quite near it.

ASPECTS OF THE HEAVENS

The immensity of the distances which separate us from the heavenly bodies makes it impossible for us to form a distinct conception of the true scale of the universe, and very difficult to conceive of the heavenly bodies in their actual relations to us. If, on looking at a body in the sky, there were any way of estimating its distance, and if our eyes were so keen that we could see the minutest features on the surface of the planets and stars, the true structure of the universe would have been obvious from the time that men began to study the heavens. A little reflection will make it obvious that if we could mount above the earth to a distance of, say, ten thousand times its diameter, so that it would no longer have any perceptible size, it would look to us, in the light of the sun, like a star in the sky. The ancients had no conception of distances like this, and so supposed that the heavenly bodies were, as they appeared, of a constitution totally different from that of the earth. We ourselves, looking at the heavens, are unable to conceive of the stars being millions of times farther than the planets. All look as if spread out on one sky at the same distance. We have to learn their actual arrangement and distances by reason.

It is from the impossibility of conceiving these enormous differences in the distances of objects on the earth and the heavens, that the real difficulty of forming a mental picture of them in their true relation arises. I shall ask the reader's careful attention in an attempt to present these relations in the simplest way, so as to connect things as they are with things as we see them.

Let us suppose the earth taken away from under our feet, leaving us hanging in mid space. We should then see the heavenly bodies—sun, moon, planets, and stars —surrounding us in every direction, up and down, east and west, north and south. The eye would rest on nothing else. As we have just explained, all these objects would seem to us to be at the same distance.

A great collection of points scattered in every direction at an equal distance from one central point must all lie upon the inner surface of a hollow sphere. It follows that, in the case supposed, the heavenly bodies will appear to us as if set in a sphere in the center of which we appear to be placed. Since one of the final objects of astronomy is to learn the directions of the heavenly bodies from us, this apparent sphere is talked about in astronomy as if it were a reality. It is called the *celestial sphere*. In the case we have supposed, with the earth out of the way, all the heavenly bodies on this sphere would at any moment seem at rest. The stars would remain apparently at rest day after day and week after week. It is true that, by watching the planets, we should in a few days or weeks, as the case might be, see their slow motion around the sun, but this would not be perceptible at once. Our first impression would be that the sphere was made of some solid, crystalline substance, and that the heavenly bodies were fastened to its inner surface. The ancients had this notion, which they

brought yet nearer the truth by fancying a number of
these spheres fitting inside of each other to represent the
different distances of the heavenly bodies.

With this conception well in mind, let us bring the
earth back under our feet. Now we have to make a draft
upon the reader's power of conception. Considered in
its relation to the magnitude of the heavens, the earth
is a mere point; yet, when we bring it into place, its
surface cuts off one half of the universe from our view,
just as an apple would cut off the view of one side of a
room from an insect crawling upon it. That half of the
celestial sphere which, being above the horizon, remains
visible is called the *visible hemisphere;* the half below,
the view of which is cut off by the earth, is called the
invisible hemisphere. Of course we could see the latter
by traveling around the earth.

Having this state of things well in mind, we must
make another draft on the reader's attention. We know
that the earth is not at rest, but rotates unceasingly
around an axis passing through its center. The natural
result of this is an apparent rotation of the celestial
sphere in the opposite direction. The earth rotates from
west toward east; hence the sphere seems to rotate from
east toward west. This real rotation of the earth, with
the apparent revolution of the stars which it causes, is
called the *diurnal motion,* because it is completed in a
day.

APPARENT DAILY REVOLUTION OF THE STARS

Our next problem is to show the connection between
the very simple conception of the rotation of the earth
and the more complicated appearance presented by the

apparent diurnal motion of the heavenly bodies which it brings about. The latter varies with the latitude of the observer upon the earth's surface. Let us begin with its appearance in our middle northern latitudes.

For this purpose we may in imagination build a hollow globe representing the celestial sphere. We may make it as large as we please, but one of thirty or forty feet in diameter would answer our purpose. Let Figure 1 be an inside view of this globe, mounted on two pivots, P and Q, so that it can turn round on them diagonally. In the middle, at O, we have a horizontal platform, NS, on which we sit. The constellations are marked on the inside of the globe, covering the whole surface, but those on the lower half are hidden from view by the platform. This platform, as is evident, represents the horizon.

The globe is now made to turn on its pivots. What will happen? We shall see the stars near the pivot P revolving around the latter as the globe turns. The stars on a certain circle KN will graze the edges of the platform, as they pass below P. Those yet farther from P will dip below the platform to a greater or less extent, according to their distance from P. Stars near the circle EF, halfway between P and Q, will perform half their course above and half below the platform. Finally, stars within the circle ST will never rise above the level of the platform at all, and will remain invisible to us.

To our eyes the celestial sphere is such a globe as this, of infinite dimensions. It seems to us to be continually revolving round a certain point in the sky as a pivot, making one revolution in nearly a day, and carrying the sun, moon, and stars with it. The stars preserve their relative positions as if fastened to the revolving celestial sphere. That is to say, if we take a photograph of them at any hour of the night, the same photograph will show their appearance at any other hour, if we only hold it in the right position.

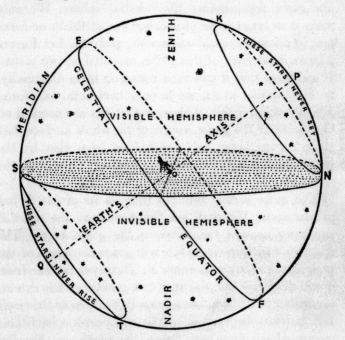

FIG. 1. *The Celestial Sphere as It Appears to Us*

The pivot corresponding to P is called the *north celestial pole*. To dwellers in middle northern latitudes, where most of us live, it is in the northern sky, nearly midway between the zenith and the northern horizon. The farther south we live, the nearer it is to the horizon, its altitude above the latter being equal to the latitude of the place where the observer stands. Quite near it is the pole star, which we shall hereafter show how to locate. To ordinary observation, the pole star seems never to move from its position. In our time it is little more than a degree from the pole, a quantity with which we need not now concern ourselves.

Opposite the north celestial pole, and therefore as far below our horizon as the north one is above, lies the *south celestial pole*.

An obvious fact is that the diurnal motion as we see it in our latitude is oblique. When the sun rises in the east it does not seem to go straight up from the horizon, but moves over toward the south at a more or less acute angle with the horizon. So when it sets, its motion relative to the horizon is again oblique.

Now, imagine that we take a pair of compasses long enough to reach the sky. We put one point on the sky at the north celestial pole, and the other point far enough from it to touch the horizon below the pole. Keeping the first point at the pole, we draw a complete circle on the celestial sphere with the other point. This circle just touches the north horizon at its lowest points and, in our northern latitudes, extends to near the zenith at its highest point. The stars within this circle never set, but only seem to perform a daily course around the pole. For this reason this circle is called the *circle of perpetual apparition*.

The stars farther south rise and set, but perform less and less of their daily course above our horizon, till we reach its south point, where they barely show themselves.

Stars yet farther south never rise at all in our latitudes. They are contained within the *circle of perpetual occultation,* which surrounds and is centered on the south celestial pole, as the circle of perpetual apparition is centered on the north one.

Figure 2 shows the principal stars of the northern heavens within the circle of perpetual apparition for the Northern States. By holding it with the month on top we shall have a view of the constellations as they are seen about eight o'clock in the evening. It also shows how to find the pole star in the center by the direction of the two outer stars or pointers in the Dipper, or Great Bear.

Now let us change our latitude and see what occurs. If we journey toward the equator, the direction of our horizon changes, and during our voyage we see the pole star constantly sinking lower and lower. As we approach the equator, it approaches the horizon, reaching it when we reach the equator. It is plain enough that the circle of perpetual apparition grows smaller until, at the equator, it ceases to exist, each pole being in our horizon. There the diurnal motion seems to us quite different from what it is here. The sun, moon, and stars, when they rise, commence their motion directly upwards. If one of them rises exactly in the east, it will pass through the zenith; one rising south of the east will pass south of the zenith; one rising north of the east, north of the zenith.

Continuing our course into the southern hemisphere, we find that the sun, while still rising in the east, generally passes the meridian to the north of the zenith. The main point of difference between the two hemispheres is that, as the sun now culminates in the north, its ap-

parent motion is not in the direction of the hands of a
watch, as with us, but in the opposite direction. In
middle southern latitudes, the northern constellations,
so familiar to us, are always below the horizon, but we

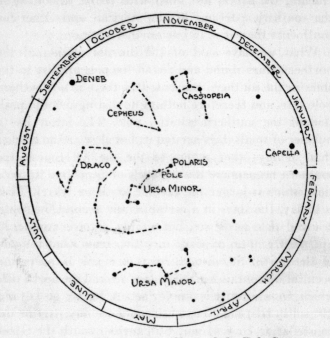

FIG. 2.   *The Northern Sky and the Pole Star*

see new ones in the south. Some of these are noted for
their beauty, the Southern Cross, for example. Indeed,
it has often been thought that the southern heavens
are more brilliant and contain more stars than the
northern ones. But this view is now found to be incor-
rect. Careful study and counts of the stars show the

number to be about the same in one hemisphere as in the other. Probably the impression we have mentioned arose from the superior clearness of the sky in the southern regions. For some reason, perhaps because of the drier climate, the air is less filled with smoke and haze in the southern portions of the African and American continents than it is in our northern regions.

What we have said of the diurnal motion of the northern stars round and round the pole applies to the stars in the southern heavens. But there is no southern pole star, and therefore nothing to distinguish the position of the southern celestial pole. The latter has a number of small stars around it, but they are no thicker than in any other region of the sky. Of course, the southern hemisphere has its circle of perpetual apparition, which is larger the farther south we travel. That is to say, the stars in a certain circle around the south celestial pole never set, but simply revolve around it, apparently in an opposite direction from what they do in the north. So, also, there is a circle of perpetual occultation containing those stars around the north pole which, in our latitudes, never set. After we go beyond 20° south latitude we can no longer see any part of the constellation Ursa Minor. Still farther south the Great Bear will only occasionally show itself to a greater or less extent above the horizon.

Could we continue our journey to the south pole we should no longer see any rising or setting of the stars. The latter would move around the sky in horizontal circles, the center or pole being at the zenith. Of course, the same thing would be true at the north pole.

III

RELATION OF TIME AND LONGITUDE

WE ALL know that a line running through any place on the earth in a north and south direction is called the meridian of that particular place. More exactly, a meridian of the earth's surface is a semicircle passing from the north to the south pole. Such semicircles pass in every direction from the north pole, and one may be drawn so as to pass through any place. The meridian of the Royal Observatory at Greenwich is now adopted by most nations, our own included, as the one from which longitudes are measured, and by which in the United States and a considerable part of Europe the clocks are set.

Corresponding to the terrestrial meridian of a place is a celestial meridian which passes from the north celestial pole through the zenith, intersects the horizon at its south point, and continues to the south pole. As the earth revolves on its axis it carries the celestial as well as the terrestrial meridian with it, so that the former, in the course of a day, sweeps over the whole celestial sphere. The appearance to us is that every point of the celestial sphere crosses the meridian in the course of a day.

Noon is the moment at which the sun passes the meridian. Before the introduction of railways, people used to set their clocks by the sun. But owing to the obliquity of the ecliptic and the eccentricity of the earth's orbit around the sun, the intervals between successive passages of the sun are not exactly equal. The consequence is that, if a clock keeps exact time, the sun will sometimes pass the meridian before and sometimes after twelve by the clock. When this was understood, a distinction was made between apparent and mean time. Apparent time is the unequal time determined by the sun; mean time is that given by a clock keeping perfect time month after month. The difference between these two is called the equation of time. Its greatest amounts are reached every year about the first of November and the middle of February. At the former time, the sun passes the meridian sixteen minutes before the clock shows twelve; in February, fourteen or fifteen minutes after twelve.

To define mean time astronomers imagine a mean sun which always moves along the celestial equator so as to pass the meridian at exactly equal intervals of time, and which is sometimes ahead of the real sun and sometimes behind it. This imaginary or mean sun determines the time of day. The subject will perhaps be a little easier if we describe things as they appear, imagining the earth to be at rest while the mean sun revolves around it, crossing the meridian of every place in succession. We thus imagine noon to be constantly traveling around the world. In our latitudes, its speed is not far from a thousand feet per second; that is to say, if it is noon at a certain place where we stand, it will one second afterward be noon about one thousand feet farther west, in another second a thousand feet yet farther west, and so on through the twenty-four hours, until noon will once more get back to where we are. The obvious result of this is that it is never the same time of day at the same moment at two places east or west of each other. As we travel west, we shall continually find our watches to be too fast for the places which we reach, while in traveling east they will be too slow. This varying time is called *local time*.

STANDARD TIME

Formerly the use of local time caused great inconvenience to travelers. Every railway had its own meridian which it ran its trains by; and the traveler was frequently liable to miss his train by not knowing the relation between his watch or a clock and the railway time. So in 1883, our present system of standard time was introduced. Under this system, standard meridians are adopted fifteen degrees apart, this being the space over which the sun passes in one hour. The time at which noon passes a standard meridian is then used throughout a zone extending seven or eight degrees on each side. This is called *standard time*. The longitudes which mark the zones are reckoned from Greenwich. It happens that Philadelphia is about seventy-five degrees in longitude, or five hours in time from Greenwich. More exactly, it is about one minute of time more than this. Thus the standard meridian which we use for the Eastern States passes a little east of Philadelphia. When mean noon reaches this meridian it is considered as twelve o'clock as far west as Ohio. An hour later, it is considered twelve o'clock in the Mississippi Valley. An hour later, it is twelve o'clock for the region of the Rocky Mountains. In yet another hour, it is twelve o'clock on the Pacific coast. Thus we use four different kinds of time, Eastern time, Central time, Mountain time, and Pacific time, differing from each other by entire hours. Using this time, the traveler has only to set his watch forward or back one hour at a time, as he travels between the Pacific and the Atlantic coast, and he will always find it correct for the region in which he is at the time.

It is by this difference of time that the longitudes of places are determined. Imagine that an observer in New York makes a tap with a telegraph key at the exact moment when a certain star crosses his meridian, and that this moment is recorded at Chicago as well as New York. When the star reaches the meridian of Chicago, the observer taps the time of its crossing over his meridian in the same way. The interval between the two taps shows the difference of longitude between the two cities.

Another method of getting the same result is for each observer to telegraph his local time to the other. The difference of the two times gives the longitude.

In this connection, it must be remembered that the heavenly bodies rise and set by local, not standard, time. Hence the time of rising and setting of the sun, given in the almanacs, will not answer to set our watches by for standard time unless we are on one of the standard meridians. One difference between these two kinds of time is that local time varies continuously as we travel east or west, while standard time varies only by jumps of one hour when we cross the boundaries of any of the four zones just described.

WHERE THE DAY CHANGES

Midnight, like noon, is continually traveling round the earth, crossing all the meridians in succession. At every crossing it inaugurates the beginning of another day on that meridian. If it is Monday at any crossing, it will be Tuesday when it gets back again. So there must be some meridian where Monday changes to Tuesday, and where every day changes into the day following. This dividing meridian, called the "date line," is determined only by custom and convenience. As colonization extended toward the east and the west men carried their count of days with them. The result was that whenever it extended so far that those going east met those going west they found their time differing by one day. What for the westward traveler was Monday was Tuesday for the eastern one. This was the case when we acquired Alaska. The Russians having reached that region by traveling east, it was found that, when we took possession by going west, our Saturday was their Sunday. This gave rise to the question whether the inhabitants, in celebrating the festivals of the Greek Church, should follow the old or the new reckoning of days. The subject was referred to the head of the church at St. Petersburg, and finally to Struve, the director of the Pulkova Observatory, the national astronomical institution of the empire. Struve made a report in favor of the American reckoning, and the change to it was duly carried out.

At the present time custom prescribes for the date line the meridian opposite that of Greenwich. This passes through the Pacific Ocean, and in its course crosses very little land—only the northeastern corner of Asia and, perhaps, some of the Fiji Islands. This fortunate circumstance prevents a serious inconvenience which might arise if the date line passed through the interior of a country. In this case the people of one city might have their time a day different from those of a neighboring city across the line. It is even conceivable that residents on two sides of the same street would have different days for Sunday. But being in the ocean, no such inconvenience follows. The date line is not necessarily a meridian of the earth, but may deviate from one side to the other in order to prevent the inconvenience we have described. Thus the inhabitants of Chatham Island have the same time as that of the neighboring island of New Zealand, although the meridian of 180° from Greenwich runs between them.

IV

HOW THE POSITION OF A HEAVENLY BODY IS DEFINED

IN THIS chapter I have to use and explain some technical terms. The ideas conveyed by them are necessary to a complete understanding of the celestial motions, and of the positions of the stars at any hour when we may wish to observe them. To the reader who desires only a general idea of celestial phenomena, this chapter will not be necessary. I must invite one who wants a knowledge more thorough than this to make a close study of the celestial sphere as it was described in our second chapter. Turning back to our first figure, we see ourselves concerned with the relation of two spheres. One of these is the real globe of the earth, on the surface of which we dwell, and which is continually carrying us around by its daily rotation. The other is the apparent sphere of the heavens, which surrounds our globe on all sides at an enormous distance, and which, although it has no reality, we are obliged to imagine in order to know where to look for the heavenly bodies. Notice that we see this sphere from its center, so that everything we see upon it appears upon its inside surface, while we see the surface of the earth from the outside.

There is a correspondence between points and circles on these two spheres. We have already shown how the axis of the earth, which marks our north and south poles, being continued in both directions through space, marks the north and south poles of the celestial sphere.

We know that the earth's equator passes around it at an equal distance from the two poles. In the same way we have an equator on the celestial sphere which passes around it at a distance of ninety degrees from either celestial pole. If it could be painted on the sky we should always see it, by day or night, in one fixed position. We can imagine exactly how it would look. It intersects the horizon in the east and west points, and is in fact the line which the sun seems to mark out in the sky by its diurnal course during the twelve hours that it is above the horizon at the equinoxes, in March or September. In our northernmost States it passes about halfway between the zenith and the south horizon, but passes nearer the zenith the farther south we are.

As we have circles of latitude parallel to the equator passing around the earth both north and south of the equator, so we have on the celestial sphere circles parallel to the celestial equator, and therefore having one or the other of the celestial poles as a center. As the parallels of latitude on the earth grow smaller and smaller toward the pole, so do these celestial circles grow smaller toward the celestial poles.

We know that longitude on the earth is measured by the position of a meridian passing from the north to the south pole through the place whose position is to be defined. The angle which this meridian makes with that through the Greenwich Observatory is the longitude of the place.

We have the same system in the heavens. Circles are imagined to pass from one celestial pole to the other in every direction, but all intersecting the equator at right angles, as shown in Figure 3. These are called *hour circles*. One of them is called the equinoctial colure, and

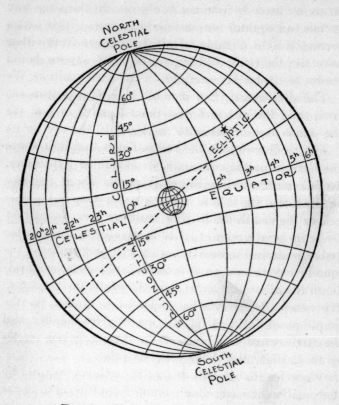

Fig. 3. *Circles of the Celestial Sphere*

is so marked in the figure. It passes through the vernal equinox, a point to be defined in the next chapter. This circle plays a part in the sky corresponding to the meridian of Greenwich on the earth's surface.

The position of a star on the celestial sphere is defined in the same way that the position of a city on the earth is defined, by its longitude and latitude. But different terms are used. In astronomy, the measure which corresponds to longitude is called *right ascension;* that which corresponds to latitude is called *declination.* We thus have the following definitions, which I must ask the reader to remember carefully.

The declination of a star is its apparent distance from the celestial equator north or south. In the figure the star is in declination 25° north.

The right ascension of a star is the angle which the hour circle passing through it makes with the equinoctial colure which passes through the vernal equinox. In the figure the star is in three hours right ascension.

The right ascension of a star is, in astronomical usage, generally expressed as so many hours, minutes, and seconds, in the way shown on Figure 3. But it may equally well be expressed in degrees, as we express the longitude of a place on the earth. The right ascension expressed in hours may be changed into degrees by the simple process of multiplication by 15. This is because the earth revolves 15° in an hour. Figure 3 also shows us that, while the degrees of latitude are nearly of the same length all over the earth, those of longitude continually diminish, slowly at first and more rapidly afterwards, from the equator toward the poles. At the equator the degree of longitude is about 69½ statute miles, but at the latitude of 45° it is only about 42 miles. At 60° it is less than 35 miles, at the pole it comes down to nothing, because there the meridians meet.

We may see that the speed of the rotation of the earth follows the same law of diminution. At the equator, 15° is about 1,000 miles. There the rotation is at the rate of 1,000 miles an hour. This is about 1,500 feet per second. But in latitude 45° the speed is diminished to little more than 1,000 feet per second. At 60°, north, it is only half that at the equator; at the poles it goes down to nothing.

In applying this system the only trouble arises from the earth's rotation. As long as we do not travel, we remain on the same circle of longitude on the earth. But by the rotation of the earth, the right ascension of any point in the sky which seems to us fixed, is continually changing. The only difference between the celestial meridian and an hour circle is that the former travels round with the earth, while the latter is fixed on the celestial sphere.

There is a strict resemblance in almost every point between the earth and the celestial sphere. As the former rotates on its axis from west to east, the latter seems to rotate from east to west. If we imagine the earth centered inside the celestial sphere with a common axis passing through them, as shown in the figure, we shall have a clear idea of the relations we wish to set forth.

If the sun, like the stars, seemed fixed on the celestial sphere from year to year, the problem of finding a star when we knew its right ascension and declination would be easier than it actually is. Owing to the annual revolution of the earth round the sun there is a continual change in the apparent position of the sphere at a given hour of the night. We must next point out the effect of this revolution.

V

THE ANNUAL MOTION OF THE EARTH AND ITS RESULTS

IT IS well known that the earth not only turns on its axis, but makes an annual revolution round the sun. The result of this motion—in fact, the phenomenon by which it is shown—is that the sun appears to make an annual revolution around the celestial sphere among the stars. We have only to imagine ourselves moving round the sun and therefore seeing the latter in different directions, to see that it must appear to us to move among the stars, which are farther than it is. It is true that the motion is not at once evident because the stars are invisible in the daytime. But the fact of the motion will be made very clear if, day after day, we watch some particular fixed star in the west. We shall find that it sets earlier and earlier every day; in other words, it is getting continually nearer and nearer the sun. More exactly, since the real direction of the star is unchanged, the sun appears to be approaching the star.

If we could see the stars in the daytime, all round the sun, the case would be yet clearer. We should see that if the sun and a star rose together in the morning the sun would, during the day, gradually work past the star in an easterly direction. Between the rising and setting it would move nearly its own diameter relative to the star. Next morning we should see that it had gotten quite away from the star, being nearly two diameters distant from it. The figure shows how this would go on at the time of the spring equinox, after March 21. This motion would continue month after month. At the end of the year the sun would have made a complete circuit of the heavens relative to the star, and we should see the two once more together.

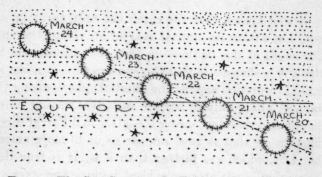

FIG. 4. *The Sun Crossing the Equator about March 21*

THE SUN'S APPARENT PATH

How the above effect is produced will be seen by Figure 5, which represents the earth's orbit round the sun, with the stars in the vast distance. When the earth is at A, we see the sun in the line AM, as if it were among the stars at M. As we carried on the earth from A to B, the sun seems to move from M to N, and so on through the year. This apparent motion of the sun in one year around the celestial sphere was noticed by the ancients, who seem to have taken much trouble to map it out. They imagined a line passing around the celestial sphere which the sun always follows in its annual course,

and which they called the *ecliptic*. They noticed that
the planets follow nearly but not exactly the same general
course as the sun among the stars. A belt extending
around on each side of the ecliptic, and broad enough
to contain all the known planets, as well as the sun, was

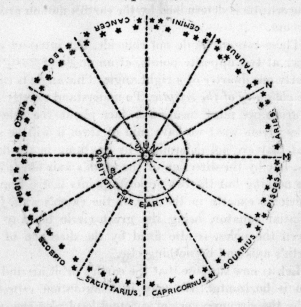

FIG. 5. *The Orbit of the Earth, and the Zodiac*

called the *zodiac*. It was divided into twelve signs, each
marked by a constellation. The sun goes through each
sign in the course of a month and through all twelve
signs in a year. Thus arose the familiar signs of the
zodiac, which bore the same names as the constellations
among which they were situated. This is not the case at
present, owing to the slow motion of precession soon to
be described.

It will be seen that the two great circles we have described spanning the entire celestial sphere are fixed in entirely different ways. The equator is determined by the direction in which the axis of the earth points, and spans the sphere midway between the two celestial poles. The ecliptic is determined by the earth's motion around the sun.

These two circles do not coincide, but intersect each other at two opposite points, at an angle of $23\frac{1}{2}°$, or nearly one quarter of a right angle. This angle is called the *obliquity of the ecliptic*. To understand exactly how it arises we must mention a fact about the celestial poles; from what we have said of them it will be seen that they are not determined by anything in the heavens, but by the direction of the earth's axis only; they are nothing but the two opposite points in the heavens which lie exactly in the line of the earth's axis. The celestial equator, being the great circle halfway between the poles, is also fixed by the direction of the earth's axis and by nothing else.

Let us now suppose that the earth's orbit around the sun is horizontal. We may in imagination represent it by the circumference of a round level platform with the sun in its center. We suppose the earth to move around the circumference of the platform with its center on the level of the platform; then, if the earth's axis were vertical, its equator would be horizontal and on a level with the platform and therefore would always be directed toward the sun in its center, as the earth made its annual course around the platform. Then, on the celestial sphere, the ecliptic determined by the course of the sun would be the same circle as the equator. The obliquity of the ecliptic arises from the fact that the earth's orbit is not vertical, as just supposed, but is inclined 23½°. The ecliptic has the same inclination to the plane of the platform; thus the obliquity is the result of the inclination of the earth's axis. An important fact connected with the subject is that, as the earth makes its revolutions around the sun, the direction of its axis remains unchanged in space; hence its

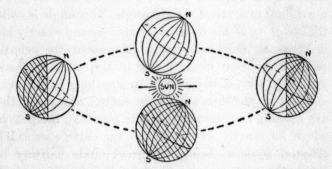

FIG. 6. *How the Obliquity of the Ecliptic Produces the Changes of Seasons*

north pole is tipped away from the sun or toward it, according to its position in the orbit. This is shown in Figure 6, which represents the platform we have supposed, with the earth's axis tipped toward the right hand. The north pole will always be tipped in this direction, whether the earth is east, west, north, or south from the sun.

To see the effect of the inclination upon the ecliptic suppose that, at noon on some twenty-first day of March, the earth should suddenly stop turning on its axis, but continue its course around the sun. What we should then see during the next three months is represented in Figure 7, in which we are supposed to be looking at the southern sky. We see the sun on the meridian, where it will at first seem to remain immovable. The figure shows the celestial equator passing through the east and west points of the horizon as already described and also the ecliptic, intersecting it at the equinox. Watching the result for a time equal to

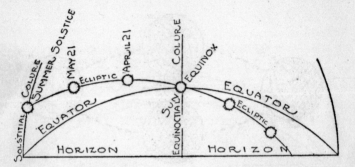

Fig. 7. *Apparent Motion of the Sun along the Ecliptic in Spring and Summer*

three of our months we should see the sun slowly make its way along the ecliptic to the point marked "summer solstice," its farthest northern point, which it would reach about June 22.

Figure 8 enables us to follow its course for three months longer. After passing the summer solstice, its course gradually carries it once more to the equator, which it again crosses about September 23. Its course during the rest of the year is the counterpart of that during the first six months. It is farthest south of the equator on December 22, and again crosses it on March

21. The dates vary a little from year to year owing to the plan of leap years.

We see that there are four cardinal points in this apparent annual course of the sun: (1) Where we have commenced our watch is the vernal equinox. (2) The point where the sun, having reached its northern limit, begins to again approach the equator. This is called the summer solstice. (3) Opposite the vernal equinox is the

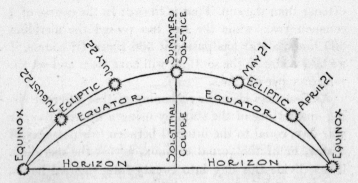

Fig. 8.   *Apparent Motion of the Sun from March till September*

autumnal equinox, which the sun passes about September 23. (4) Opposite the summer solstice is the point where the sun is farthest south. This is called the winter solstice.

The hour circles which pass from one celestial pole to the other through these points at right angles to the equator are called *colures*. That which passes through the vernal equinox is the equinoctial colure, from which right ascensions are counted as already described. The one at right angles to it is called the solstitial colure.

Let us now show the relation of the constellations to the seasons and the time of day. Suppose that to-day the sun and a star passed the meridian at the same moment; to-morrow the sun will be nearly a degree to the east of the star, which shows that the star will pass the meridian nearly four minutes sooner than the sun will. This will continue day after day throughout the entire year until the two will again pass the meridian at about the same moment. Thus the star will have passed once oftener than the sun. That is to say: In the course of a common year, while the sun has passed the meridian 365 times, a star has passed it 366 times. Of course, if we take a star in the south, it will have risen and set the same number of times.

Astronomers keep the reckoning of this different rising and setting of the stars by using a sidereal day, or star day, equal to the interval between two passages of a star, or of the vernal equinox, across the meridian. They divide this day into twenty-four sidereal hours, and these into minutes and seconds, according to the usual plan. They also use sidereal clocks which gain about three minutes and fifty-six seconds per day on the ordinary clocks and thus show sidereal time. Sidereal noon is the moment at which the vernal equinox crosses the meridian of the place. The clock is then set at 0 hours, 0 minutes, and 0 seconds. Thus set and regulated, the sidereal clock keeps time with the apparent rotation of the celestial sphere, so that the astronomer has only to look at his clock to see, by day or by night, what stars are on the meridian and what the positions of the constellations are.

THE SEASONS

If the earth's axis were perpendicular to the plane of the ecliptic, the latter would coincide with the equator, and we should have no difference of seasons the year round. The sun would always rise in the exact east and set in the exact west. There would be only a very slight change in the temperature arising from the fact that the earth is a little nearer the sun in January than in July. Owing to the obliquity of the ecliptic it follows that, while the sun is north of the equator, which is the case from March to September, the sun shines upon the northern hemisphere during a greater time of each day, and at a greater angle, than on the southern hemisphere. In the southern hemisphere the opposite is the case. The sun shines longer from September till March than it does on the northern hemisphere. Thus we have winter in the northern hemisphere when it is summer in the southern, and vice versa.

RELATIONS BETWEEN REAL AND APPARENT MOTIONS

Before going farther let us recapitulate the phenomena we have described from the two points of view: one, that of the real motions of the earth; the other, that of the apparent motions of the heavens, to which the real motions give rise.

The real diurnal motion is the turning of the earth on its axis.

The apparent diurnal motion is that which the stars appear to have in consequence of the earth's rotation.

The real annual motion is that of the earth round the sun.

The apparent annual motion is that of the sun around the celestial sphere among the stars.

By the real diurnal motion the plane of our horizon is carried past the sun or a star.

We then say that the sun or star rises or sets, as the case may be.

About March twenty-first of every year the plane of the earth's equator passes from the north to the south of the sun, and about September twenty-third it repasses toward the north.

We then say that the sun crosses to the north of the equator in March, and to the south in September.

In June of every year the plane of the earth's equator is at the greatest distance south of the sun, and in December at the greatest distance north.

We say in the first case that the sun is at the northern solstice, and in the second that it is at the southern solstice.

The earth's axis is tipped twenty-three and a half degrees from the perpendicular to the earth's orbit.

The apparent result is that the ecliptic is inclined twenty-three and a half degrees to the celestial equator.

During June and the other summer months the northern hemisphere of the earth is tipped toward the sun. Places in north latitude, as they are carried round by the turning of the earth, are then in sunlight during more than half their course; those in south latitude less.

The result as it appears to us is that the sun is more than half the time above the horizon, and that we have the hot weather of summer, while in the southern hemisphere the days are short, and the season is winter.

During our winter months the case is reversed. The southern hemisphere is then tipped toward the sun, and the northern hemisphere away from it. Consequently, summer and long days are the order in the southern and the reverse in the northern hemisphere.

THE YEAR AND THE PRECESSION OF THE EQUINOXES

We most naturally define the year as the interval of time in which the earth revolves around the sun. From what we have said, there are two ways of ascertaining its length. One is to find the interval between two passages of the sun past the same star. The other is to find the interval between two passages of the sun past the same equinox, that is, across the equator. If the latter were fixed among the stars the two intervals would be equal. But it was found by the ancient astronomers, from observations extending through several centuries, that these two methods do not give the same length of year. It takes the sun about eleven minutes longer to make the circuit of the stars than to make the circuit of the equinoxes. This shows that the equinoxes steadily shift their position among the stars from year to year. This shift is called the precession of the equinoxes. It does not arise from anything going on in the heavens, but only from a slow change in the direction of the earth's axis from year to year as it moves around the sun.

If we should suppose the platform in Figure 6 to last for six or seven thousand years, and the earth to make its six or seven thousand revolutions around it, we should find that, at the end of this time, the north end of the axis of the earth, instead of being tipped toward our right hand, as shown in the figure, would be tipped directly toward us. At the end of another six or seven thousand years it would be tipped toward our left; at the end of a third such period it would be tipped away from us, and at the end of a fourth, or about twenty-six thousand years in all, it would have gotten back to its original direction.

Since the celestial poles are determined by the direction of the earth's axis, this change in the direction of the axis makes them slowly go around a circle in the heavens, having a radius of about twenty-three and a half degrees. At the present time the pole star is a little more than a degree from the pole. But the pole is gradually approaching it and will pass by it in about two hundred years. In twelve thousand years from now the pole will be in the constellation Lyra, about five degrees from the bright star Vega of that constellation. In the time of the ancient Greeks their navigators did not recognize any pole star at all, because what is now such was then ten or twelve degrees from the pole, the latter having been between it and the constellation of the Great Bear. It was the latter which they steered by.

It follows from all this that, since the celestial equator is the circle midway between the two poles, there must be a corresponding shift in its position among the stars. The effect of this shift during the past two thousand years is shown in Figure 9. Since the equinoxes are the points of crossing of the ecliptic and the equator, they also change in consequence of this motion. It is thus that the precession of the equinoxes arises.

The two kinds of year we have described are called *tropical* and *sidereal*. The tropical year is the interval between two returns of the sun to the equinox. Its length is 365 days 5 hours 48 minutes 46 seconds.

Since the seasons depend upon the sun's being north or south of the equator, the tropical year is that used in the reckoning of time. The ancient astronomers found that its length was about three hundred and sixty-five and one quarter days. As far back as the time of Ptolemy the length of the year was known even

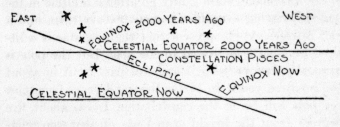

FIG. 9.   *Precession of the Equinoxes*

more exactly than this, and found to be a few minutes less than three hundred and sixty-five and one quarter days. The Gregorian Calendar, which nearly all civilized nations now use, is based upon a close approximation to this length of the year.

The sidereal year is the interval between two passages of the sun past the same star. Its length is three hundred and sixty-five days six hours and nine minutes.

According to the Julian calendar, which was in use in Christendom until 1582, the year was considered to be exactly 365¼ days. This, it will be seen, was 11 minutes 14 seconds more than the true length of the tropical year. Consequently, the seasons were slowly changing in the course of centuries. In order to obviate this, and have a year whose average length was as nearly as possible correct, a decree was passed by Pope Gregory XIII by which, in three centuries out of four, a day was dropped from the Julian calendar. According to the latter, the closing year of every century would be a leap year. In the Gregorian calendar 1600 was still to remain a leap year, but 1500, 1700, 1800, and 1900 were all common years.

The Gregorian calendar was adopted immediately by all Catholic countries, and from time to time by Protestant countries also, so that for the past 150 years it has been universal in both.

Part II

THE TELESCOPE

I

THE REFRACTING TELESCOPE

THERE is no branch of science more interesting to the public than that with which the telescope is concerned. I assume that the reader wishes to have an intelligent idea as to what a telescope is and what can be seen with it. In its most complete form, as used by the astronomer in his observatory, the instrument is quite complex. But there are a few main points about it which can be mastered in a general way by a little close attention. After mastering these points, the visitor to an observatory will examine the instrument with much more satisfaction than he can when he knows nothing about it.

An important function of a telescope, as we all know, is to make distant objects look nearer to us; to see an object miles away as if it were, perhaps, only as many yards. The optical appliances by which this is effected can be readily understood. They are made with large well-polished lenses, of the same kind as those used in a pair of spectacles, differing from the latter only in their size and general perfection. There are two ways in which the light coming from the object may be collected: one way is by passing the light through a set of lenses, and the other, by reflecting it from a concave mirror. Thus we have two different kinds of telescope, one called refracting, the other reflecting. We begin with the former.

THE LENSES OF A TELESCOPE

The lenses of a refracting telescope comprise two combinations or systems; one is the object-glass, or "objective," which forms the image of a distant object in the focus of the instrument; the other is the eye-piece, with which this image is viewed.

The objective is the really difficult and delicate part of the instrument. Its construction involves more refined skill than that of all the other parts together. How great is the natural aptitude required may be judged from the fact that a half century ago there was but one man in the world in whose ability to make a perfect object-glass of the largest size astronomers everywhere would have felt confidence. This man was Alvan Clark, of whom we shall soon speak.

The object-glass, as commonly made, consists of two large lenses. The power of the telescope depends altogether on the diameter of these lenses, which is called the *aperture* of the telescope. The aperture may vary from three or four inches, in the little telescope which one has in his house, to more than three feet in the great telescope of the Yerkes Observatory. One reason why the power of the telescope depends on the diameter of the object-glass is that in order to see an object magnified a certain number of times in its natural brightness, we need a quantity of light expressed by the square of the magnifying power. For example, if we have a magnifying power of one hundred, we should need ten thousand times the light. I do not mean that this quantity of light is always necessary; it is not so, because we can commonly see an object with less than

its natural illumination. Still, we need a certain amount
of light, or it will be too dim.

In order that distinct vision of a distant object may
be secured in the telescope, the one great essential is
that the object-glass should bring all the rays coming
from any one point of the object observed to the same
focus. If this is not brought about; if different rays
come to slightly different foci, then the object will look
blurred, as if it were seen through a pair of spectacles
which did not suit our eyes. Now, a single lens, no matter of what sort of glass we make it, will not bring rays
to the same focus. The reader is doubtless aware that
ordinary light, whether coming from the sun or a star,
is of a countless multitude of different colors, which can
be separated by passing the light through a triangular
prism. These colors range from red at one end of the
scale, through yellow, green, and blue, to violet at the
other. A single lens brings these different rays to different foci; the red farthest from the object-glass; the
violet nearest to it. This separation of the rays is called
dispersion.

The astronomers of two centuries ago found it impossible to avoid the dispersion of a lens. About 1750,
Dollond, of London, found that it was possible to correct this defect by using two different kinds of glass,
the one crown glass and the other flint glass. The principle by which this is done is very simple. Crown glass
has nearly the same refracting power as flint, but it has
nearly twice the dispersive power. So Dollond made
an objective of two lenses, a section of which is shown in
the figure. First there was a convex lens of crown glass,
which is of the usual construction. Combined with this

is a concave lens of flint glass. These two lenses, being of opposite curvatures, act on the light in opposite directions. The crown glass tends to bring the light to a focus, while the flint, being concave, would make the rays diverse. If it were used alone, we should find that the rays passing through it, instead of coming to a focus, diverge farther and farther from a focus, in different directions. Now, the flint glass is made with but little more than half the power of the crown. This

FLINT GLASS

CROWN GLASS

FIG. 10. *Section of the Object-glass of a Telescope*

half power is sufficient to neutralize the dispersion of the crown; but it does not neutralize much more than half the refraction. The combined result is that all the rays passing through the combination are brought nearly to one focus, which is about twice as far away as the focus of the crown alone.

I say brought *nearly* to one focus. It happens, unfortunately, that the combined action of the two glasses is such that it is impossible to bring all the rays of the various colors absolutely to the same focus. The larger the telescope, the more serious the defect. If you look at the moon or a bright star through any large refracting telescope, you will see it surrounded by a blue or purple fringe. The two lenses cannot bring the blue or violet light to the same focus with the other colors.

By the action of the objective, in thus bringing rays to a focus, the image of a distant object is formed in the focal plane. This is a plane passing through the focus at right angles to the axis or line of sight of the telescope.

What is meant by the image formed by a telescope can be seen by looking into the ground glass of a camera with the photographer, as he sets his instrument for a picture. You there see a face or a distant landscape pictured on the ground glass. To all intents and purposes the camera is a small telescope, and the ground glass, or the point where the sensitive plate is to be fixed to take a picture, is the focal plane. We may state the matter in the reverse direction by saying that the telescope is a large camera of long focus, with which we can take photographs of the heavens as the photographer takes ordinary pictures with the camera.

Sometimes we can better comprehend what an object is by understanding what it is not. In the celebrated moon hoax of a century ago, there was a statement which illustrates the point. The writer who perpetrated this joke on many credulous readers said that Sir John Herschel had observed the moon with such enormous magnifying power that there was not light enough for the image to be visible. It was then suggested to him that the image should be illuminated by artificial light. This was done with such brilliant success that animals in the moon were made visible through the telescope. If many people, even those of the greatest intelligence, had not been deceived by this, I should hardly deem it necessary to say that the image of an object formed by a telescope is such that, in the very nature of things, extraneous light cannot aid in its formation. Its effectiveness does not proceed from its being a real image, but only from the fact that all the rays from any one point of a distant object meet in a corresponding point of the image and there diverge again, just as if a picture of the object were placed in the focal plane. The fact is that the term picture is perhaps a little better one than image to apply to this representation of the object, only the picture is formed by light and nothing else.

If an image or picture of the object is thus formed so as to stand out before our eyes, one may ask why an eyepiece is necessary to view it; why the observer cannot stand behind the picture, look toward the objective, and see the picture hanging in the air, as it were. He can really do so if he holds a ground glass in the focal plane, as the photographer does with the camera. He can thus see the image formed on the glass. If he looks into the object-glass he can see it without any eyepiece. But only a very small portion of it will be visible at any one point, and the advantage over looking directly at the object will be slight. To see it to advantage an eyepiece must be used. This is nothing more than a little eye glass, essentially of the same kind that the watchmaker uses to examine the works of a watch. The shorter the focus of the eyepiece, the more closely the examination can be made.

The question is often asked, how great is the magnifying power of some celebrated telescope? The answer is that the magnifying power depends not only on the object-glass but on the eyepiece. The shorter the focus of the eyepiece, the greater is the magnifying power. Astronomical telescopes are supplied with quite a large collection of eyepieces, varying from the lowest to the highest power, according to the needs of the observer.

So far as the geometric principle goes, we can get any magnifying power we please on any telescope, however small. By viewing the image with an ordinary microscope, such as is used by physicians, we might give a little four-inch telescope the magnification of Herschel's great reflectors. But there are many practical difficulties in carrying the magnification of any instrument above a certain point. First there is the want of light in seeing the surface of an object. If we look at Saturn with a three-inch telescope, using a magnifying power of several hundred times, the planet seems dim and indistinct. But this is not the only difficulty in using a high magnifying power with a small telescope. The nature of light is such that as a general rule we can get no advantage in carrying the magnification above fifty, or one hundred at the most, for each inch of aperture. That is to say, with a three-inch telescope we should gain no advantage by using a power much above one hundred and fifty, and certainly none above three hundred.

But there is still another trouble, which annoys the astronomer more than all others. It is the blurring caused by the atmosphere, which is known as "bad seeing."

We see a heavenly body through a thickness of atmosphere which, were it all compressed to the density that it has around us, would be equal to about six miles. We know that when we look at a body six miles away we see its outlines softened and blurred. This is mainly because the atmosphere through which the rays have to pass is in constant turmoil, causing an irregular refraction which makes the body look wavy and tremulous. The softened and blurred effect thus produced is magnified in a telescope as many times as the object itself. The result is that as we increase the magnifying power we increase a certain indistinctness in the vision in the same proportion. The amount of this indistinctness depends very much on the condition of the air. The astronomer having this in mind tries to find locations for large telescopes where the air is steady, so that the heavenly bodies will look sharp when seen through it.

We frequently see calculations showing how near the moon can be brought to us by using some high magnifying power. For example, with a power of 1,000 we see it as if it were 240 miles away; with about 5,000, as if it were 48 miles away. This calculation is quite correct so far as the apparent size of any object on the moon is concerned, but it takes no account of either the imperfections of the telescope or the bad effect produced by the atmosphere. The result of both of these defects is that such calculations do not give a correct idea of the truth. I doubt whether any astronomer with any telescope now in existence could gain a great advantage, in the study of such an object as the moon or a planet, by carrying his magnification above a thousand, unless on very rare occasions in an atmosphere of unusual stillness.

MOUNTING OF THE TELESCOPE

Those who have never used a telescope are apt to think that the work of observing with it is simply to point it at a heavenly body and examine the latter through it.* But let us try the experiment of pointing a great telescope at a star. A result which perhaps we had not thought of comes immediately to our attention. The star, instead of remaining in the field of view of the telescope, that is to say, in the small circular portion of the sky which the telescope shows, very soon passes out of the field. This is because, as the earth revolves on its axis, the star seems to move in the opposite direction. This motion is multiplied as many times as the telescope magnifies. With a high power, the star is out of the field before we have time to examine it.

Then it must be remembered that the field of view is also magnified in the same way, so that it is smaller than it appears, in proportion to the magnifying power. For example, if a magnification of one thousand be used, the field of view of an ordinary telescope would be about two minutes in angular measure, a patch of the sky so small that to the naked eye it would look like a mere point. It would be as if we were looking at a star through a hole one eighth of an inch in diameter in the roof of a house eighteen feet high. If we imagine ourselves looking through such a hole and trying to see a star we shall readily realize how difficult will be the problem of finding it and of following it in its motion.

This difficulty is overcome by suitably mounting

---

*The writer recalls that when James Lick was founding the observatory which has since become so celebrated, the great telescope was the only feature which seemed to interest him, and his plan was to devote nearly all the funds to making the largest lens possible. He did not see why such complicated mechanical apparatus as that used by astronomers was necessary, until the exacting requirements for precise observations with a great telescope were explained to him.

the telescope, so that it turns on two axes, at right angles to each other. By the *mounting* is meant the whole system of machinery by the aid of which a telescope is pointed at a star and made to follow it in its diurnal motion. In order not to distract the attention of the reader by beginning a study of the instrument with a view of all the details, we first give an outline, showing

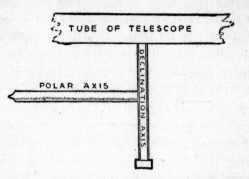

Fig. 11.   *Axes on Which a Telescope Turns*

the relation of the axes on which the telescope turns. The principal axis, called the polar axis, is adjusted so as to be parallel to the axis of the earth, and therefore to point at the celestial pole. Then, as the earth turns from west toward east, a clockwork connected with this axis turns the instrument from east toward west, with an equal motion. Thus the rotation of the earth is neutralized, as it were, by the corresponding rotation of the telescope in the opposite direction. When the instrument is pointed at a star and the clockwork set going, the star when once found will remain in the field of view.

In order that a telescope may be directed at any point of the heavens at pleasure, there must be another axis, at right angles to the polar axis. This is called the declination axis. It passes through a sheath fixed to the upper end of the polar axis so as to form a cross like the letter T. By turning the telescope on the two axes, we can point it wherever we choose.

Since the polar axis is parallel to the earth's axis, its inclination to the horizon is equal to the latitude of the place. In our latitudes, especially in the southern portions of the United States, it will be nearer horizontal than vertical. But in the observatories of northern Europe, it is more nearly vertical.

It will be seen that the contrivance we have described does not solve the problem of bringing a star into the field of view of the telescope, or as we commonly say, of finding it. We might grope round for minutes or even hours without succeeding in this. There are two processes by which a star may be found:

Every telescope for astronomical purposes is supplied with a smaller telescope fastened to the lower end of its tube, and called the *finder*. This finder is of low magnifying power, and therefore has a large field of view. By sighting along the outside of the tube, the observer, if he can see the star, can point the finder at it so nearly that it will be in the field of view of the latter. Having found it, he moves the telescope so that the object shall be seen in the center of the field. Having brought it there, it is in the field of view of the main telescope.

But most of the objects which the astronomer has to observe are totally invisible to the naked eye. He must, therefore, have some means of pointing the telescope at a star which he cannot see without it. This is done by graduated circles, one of .which is attached to each axis. One of these circles has degrees and fractions of a degree marked upon it, so as to show the declination of that point in the heavens at which the telescope is pointed. The other, attached to the polar axis, and called the hour circle, is divided into twenty-four hours, and these again into sixty minutes each. When the astronomer wishes to find a star, he simply looks at the sidereal clock, subtracts the right ascension of the star from the sidereal time, and thus gets its "hour angle" at the moment, or its distance east or west of the meridian. He sets the declination circle at the declination of the star, that is, he turns the telescope until the degree on the circle seen through a magnifying apparatus is equal to the declination of the star; and then he turns the instrument on the polar axis until the hour circle reads its hour angle. Then, starting his clockwork, he has only to look into the telescope, and there is the object.

If all this seems a complicated operation to the reader, he has only to visit an observatory and see how simply it is all done. He may thus in a few minutes gain a practical idea of sidereal time, hour angle, declination, and similar terms, which will make the whole subject much clearer than any mere description.

THE MAKING OF TELESCOPES

Let us return to some interesting matters, mostly historical, connected with the making of telescopes. The great difficulty, which requires special native skill of the rarest kind, is, as we have already intimated, that of constructing the object-glass. The slightest deviation from the proper form—a defect consisting in some part of the object-glass being too thin by a hundred thousandth part of an inch—would spoil the image.

The skill of the optician who figures the glass, that is to say, who polishes it into the proper shape, is by no means all that is required. The making of large disks of glass of the necessary uniformity and purity is a practical problem of equal difficulty. Any deviation from perfect uniformity in the glass will be as injurious to its performance as a defect in its figure.

At the beginning of the nineteenth century, it was difficult to make flint glass of the necessary uniformity. This substance contains a considerable amount of lead, which, during the process of melting the glass, would sink toward the bottom of the pot, thus making the bottom portion of greater refracting power than the upper portion. The result was that, at that time, a telescope of four or five inches aperture was considered of great size. Quite early in the century, Guinand, a Swiss, found a process by which larger disks of flint glass could be made. Perhaps his success lay only in the constant and vigorous stirring of the melted glass while it was being fused in the pot.

To utilize these disks required an optician of corresponding skill to grind and polish them into proper shape. Such an artist was found in the person of Fraunhofer, of Munich, who, about 1820, made telescopes as large as nine inches aperture. He did not stop here, but, about 1840, succeeded in making two telescopes with objectives fifteen English inches in diameter. These instruments, far exceeding any before made, were at the time regarded as marvelous. One of them was acquired by the Pulkova Observatory in Russia; the other was acquired by the Harvard Observatory where, after a lapse of more than half a century, it is still in efficient use.

After Fraunhofer's death, a worthy successor appeared where none would have thought of looking for him, in the person of Alvan Clark, portrait painter of Cambridgeport, Mass. The fact that this man, with scarcely the elements of technical education and without training in the use of optical instruments, accomplished what he did, illustrates in a striking way the importance of native talent. He seemed to have an intuitive conception of the nature of the problem, coupled with extraordinary acuteness of vision in solving it. Moved by that irrepressible impulse which is a mark of genius, he purchased in Europe the rough disks of optical glass necessary to make small telescopes, and succeeded in making one of four inches aperture to his satisfaction.

When the excellence of his lenses had gained him recognition Clark proceeded to make the largest refracting telescope that had ever been known. This was one of eighteen inches diameter, which was completed about 1860 for the University of Mississippi. While this telescope was being tested at his workshop, George B. Clark, his son, observed the companion of Sirius, which had been known to exist by its attraction on Sirius, but had never been seen by human eye. The breaking out of the Civil War prevented the University of Mississippi from taking the telescope, which was acquired by citizens of Chicago. It is now the principal instrument of the Dearborn Observatory, in Evanston.

GREAT REFRACTING TELESCOPES

The making of disks of glass of larger and larger size was continued in England, and by Feil of Paris, son-in-law of Guinand. With this glass Clark made larger and larger telescopes. First was the twenty-six-inch telescope for the Naval Observatory at Washington and a similar one for the University of Virginia. Then followed a still larger instrument, thirty inches in diameter, for the Observatory of Pulkova, Russia. Next was completed the thirty-six-inch instrument of the Lick Observatory, in California.

After the death of Feil, the business was taken up by Mantois, who made optical glass of a purity and uniformity that no one before him had ever approached. He furnished the disks with which the Clarks figured the objective for the great telescope of the Yerkes Observatory at Williams Bay, Wisconsin. This telescope is forty inches in diameter, and is the largest refracting telescope in the world.

In recent times, the manufacture of optical glass has been greatly improved both in America and abroad. A considerable number of experts have demonstrated their ability to fashion this glass into large lenses of the finest quality. More than a dozen refracting telescopes having apertures of twenty-six inches or more are in use in the study of the heavens in various parts of the world.

Remarkable improvements have been accomplished in the mechanical features also. The visitor in the modern observatory is impressed quite as much by the facility with which the views of the heavens are obtained as with the excellence of the views. While the great telescope is so nicely balanced that it can be easily moved by hand, the quick motions are likely to be made by motor. When it is desired to turn the telescope to a new object, the astronomer presses buttons. The telescope swings to the new position. The dome revolves to place the slit correctly for looking out in the new direction; and the floor of the dome, or else the observing platform, rises or falls to bring the observer to the new position of the eyepiece.

For many investigations with large telescopes, the eyepiece is removed, and auxiliary apparatus is attached in its place. It may be a plate holder for photographic study of the heavens, or a spectroscope for analyzing the light of the celestial bodies, or a special device for recording the intensity of their radiation. An important function of the telescope is to gather the light and to concentrate it at the focus where it may be studied in these and other ways. Some telescopes, such as the tower telescopes of the Mount Wilson Observatory are fixed. Moving mirrors direct the light of the celestial body steadily toward the telescope which brings it to focus in the laboratory below.

II

THE REFLECTING TELESCOPE

IN THE refracting telescope, as we have seen, the objective is a lens, or combination of lenses, placed at the upper end of the tube. It refracts the starlight to a focus near the lower end of the tube, forming there an image of the star, which may be viewed with the eyepiece, or photographed, or otherwise studied. The first telescopes to be employed, by Galileo and others more than three centuries ago, were refractors. This type of telescope, in the improved achromatic form, still has the most general use.

In the reflecting telescope the objective is a concave mirror placed at the lower end of the tube. It reflects the starlight back to a focus near the upper end of the tube. Here enters a difficulty which must be overcome. To see the image the observer must look into the mirror. If he leans over the top of the tube to do so, he will be in his own light. His head and shoulders will cut off much of the incoming starlight. Some means must be found for getting the focal point out of the tube where the image of the star can be observed advantageously. Different ways of doing this have resulted in several different forms of the reflecting telescope. Two forms, the Newtonian and the Cassegrainian, are in use at present.

The Newtonian form of reflecting telescope employs

a small diagonal mirror placed just inside the focus in the center of the tube near its upper end. This mirror, whose reflecting surface makes an angle of 45° with the axis of the telescope, receives the converging beam of light from the large mirror and reflects it laterally to the side of the tube. Here the image is viewed with an ordinary eyepiece, or it may be photographed.

Observations with the Newtonian reflector are made, therefore, near the upper end of the tube. The observer looks through the eyepiece in a direction at right angles to the direction of the star he is examining. With large reflectors the observing platform, which is attached to the revolving dome opposite the slit, is easily raised or lowered to place the observer in the required position for any pointing of the telescope.

The Cassegrainian form has a smaller, slightly convex mirror between the principal mirror and its focus. The small mirror reflects the converging beam of light back again toward the large mirror through an opening in its center to focus immediately behind it, where the eyepiece is placed. With this type of telescope the observer looks directly toward the object he is viewing, as with the refractor. Many reflecting telescopes can be employed in either the Newtonian or Cassagrainian form.

Reflecting telescopes came into extensive use two centuries ago, although the principles of the different forms had been explained fifty years before by Newton, Cassegrain, and others. Sir William Herschel made many reflecting telescopes and used some of them in his celebrated explorations of the heavens. About a century ago, Lord Rosse, Irish amateur astronomer, possessed a reflecting telescope having a mirror six feet in diameter, the leviathan of its time; in fact, it was unsurpassed in size by any other telescope until very recent years. This great telescope is remembered especially because it showed for the first time the spiral structure of some of those remote celestial objects which came to be known, therefore, as spiral nebulae.

The mirrors of the early reflecting telescopes were made of speculum metal. When their surfaces tarnished, it was necessary to refigure them. Moreover, the mechanical parts of the great telescopes of Herschel, Rosse, and others were exceedingly crude in comparison with modern ones. They could not be made to follow the celestial bodies faithfully in their westward motion, which is prerequisite for photography or, in fact, for about every type of astronomical research of the present day.

Some fifty years ago, glass replaced speculum metal for the mirrors. The circular block of glass having one surface figured in the required shape is the foundation for the mirror itself—a thin silver coat on the curved surface of the glass. When the silver coat becomes dull, it can be removed and easily replaced by a new coat. The great telescopes of to-day have silver-on-glass mirrors.

The 100-inch reflector of the Mount Wilson Observatory, in California, is the largest telescope in operation in the world. Its great mirror is a circular block of silvered glass slightly more than a hundred inches in diameter and a little more than a foot thick. The glass itself weighs four and a half tons. This telescope is housed in a dome a hundred feet in diameter.

Next in size is the 72-inch reflector of the Dominion Astrophysical Observatory, in Victoria. It is rivaled by the 70-inch reflector of the Perkins Observatory, near Delaware, Ohio, and will be slightly surpassed by the reflecting telescope now under construction for the University of Toronto. There are several 5-foot re-

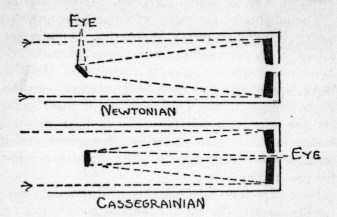

Fig. 12. *Newtonian and Cassegrainian Forms of the Reflecting Telescope*

flectors. One at the Mount Wilson Observatory has been in service for a quarter of a century. A new one of this size at the southern station of the Harvard Observatory, at Mazelspoort, South Africa, will powerfully promote the photographic studies of the southern skies.

Greatest of all is the 200-inch reflecting telescope under construction for the California Institute of Technology. Fused quartz will take the place of glass for its great mirror. Quartz is subject to less distortion by temperature variations, and it bends less under its own weight. The disk of quartz will be nearly seventeen feet across and two feet thick. Having twice the diameter of the greatest telescope now in use, and four times its light-gathering power, the new telescope will nevertheless be only a third longer. The great mirror will focus the starlight at the distance of sixty feet above its surface. This telescope will be located at a favorable site within convenient distance of Pasadena.

III

ONE of the greatest advances in astronomy was brought about by the application of photography in the study of the heavenly bodies. Back in the early '40's of the last century, Draper, of New York, succeeded in making a daguerreotype of the moon. With the invention of a better process, Bond, of the Harvard Observatory, and Rutherfurd, of New York, began to apply the art to the moon and stars. The attempts of these pioneers do not, of course, compare favorably with modern celestial photographs, although Rutherfurd brought his work to such perfection that his photographs of the Pleiades and other clusters of stars are still of value in astronomy.

A photograph of the stars can be made by an ordinary camera if we only mount it like an equatorial telescope so that it shall follow the star in its diurnal motion. A very few minutes' exposure will suffice to take a picture of more stars than can be seen by the naked eye; in fact, with a large camera, this will not require a minute. But what is generally used by the astronomer is a photographic telescope. Any ordinary telescope will serve the purpose, if suitable correcting devices are added, but in order to get the best results the object-glass of the telescope must be especially made to bring to a focus the violet and blue rays of light to which the photographic film is most sensitive.

Refracting telescopes intended for photography are frequently made shorter than visual telescopes of the same aperture, so that they may command a greater area of the sky at one time. To provide greater distinctness of the view over the larger area, and also to reduce the color blurring, their objectives are sometimes made of two pairs of lenses. Such telescopes are known, therefore, as doublets. An example is the 10-inch Bruce doublet with which Barnard secured his unsurpassed photographs of the Milky Way and of comets. The largest is the 24-inch doublet of the Harvard Observatory, which has added greatly to our knowledge of the southern celestial hemisphere. Reflecting telescopes, inasmuch as their objectives are perfectly achromatic, serve equally well for visual and for photographic researches.

To-day, the photographic plate has in large measure replaced the eye at the telescope. Clear skies are utilized for the collection of photographs, and these permanent records can be studied deliberately. It often happens after the discovery of some object of special interest, such as a new planet or a new star, that astronomers are able to trace the history of the object for many years before its discovery on earlier photographs of that region of the sky. This was the case with the recently discovered planet Pluto.

In earlier times, astronomers recorded the appearance of the sun with its spots, of the eclipsed sun, of planets, comets, nebulæ, and other celestial objects, by drawings as accurately as possible. These drawings required a long time to make, and they contained the personal bias of the artist. Sometimes two drawings of the same object by two astronomers bore only slight resemblance one to the other, or, as it turned out later, to the original. By photography we secure a more faithful representation of the celestial object, and often in a much shorter time.

One of the greatest advantages of celestial photography is that the plate with long exposure depicts many features of the heavens which the eye can discern only imperfectly or not at all. Some of the nebulæ, for example, which the photographs show very clearly are invisible to the eye at the largest telescope. The photograph of a very faint celestial object may require an exposure of many hours' duration, requiring high accuracy in the moving parts of the telescope, and skill and patience on the part of the astronomer, to produce a clear picture.

I

AN INTRODUCTORY GLANCE AT THE SOLAR SYSTEM

WE HAVE shown how this comparatively small family of bodies, on one of which we dwell, forms as it were a little colony by itself. Small though it be when compared with the whole universe as a standard, it is for us the most important part of the universe. Before proceeding to a description of the various features of the solar system in detail we must take a general view to show of what kind of bodies it is formed and how it is made up.

First of all we have the sun, the great shining central body, shedding warmth and light on all the others and keeping the whole system together by virtue of its powerful attraction.

Next we have the planets, which revolve round the sun in their regular orbits, and of which our earth is one. The word planet means *wanderer*, a term applied in ancient times because these bodies, instead of keeping their places among the fixed stars, seemed to wander about among them. The planets are divided into two quite distinct classes, termed *major* and *minor*.

The major planets are nine in number and are generally, next to the sun, the largest bodies of the system. For the most part their distances from the sun are arranged in a close approach to a certain regular

order, ranging from nearly forty millions of miles in the case of Mercury, the nearest one, to nearly four thousand millions in the case of Pluto. The latter averages a hundred times as far from the sun as Mercury. Still wider is the range of their times of revolution. Mercury performs its circuit round the sun in less than three of our months. Pluto takes nearly two hundred and fifty years for his long journey.

The major planets are separated into two groups, with quite a broad gap between the groups. The inner group is composed of four planets much smaller, in general, than the outer ones; all four together would not make a body one quarter the size of Uranus in the outer group.

In the gap between the two groups revolve the minor planets, or *asteroids* as they are commonly called. They are very small as compared with the major planets. So far as we know they are all situated in a quite wide belt ranging between a little more than the distance of the earth from the sun out to nearly ten times that distance. For the most part they are about three or four times as far from the sun as the earth is. They are also distinguished from the major planets by their far greater number; considerably more than a thousand are now known, and new discoveries are continually being made at such a rate that no one can set any exact limit to them.

A third class of bodies in the solar system comprises the *satellites*, or *moons*. Several of the major planets have one or more of these small bodies revolving round them, and therefore accompanying them in their revolution around the sun. The two innermost planets, Mer-

cury and Venus, have no satellites. In the case of the other planets, their number ranges from one (our moon) to nine each, which form the retinues of Jupiter and Saturn. Each major planet, Mercury and Venus excepted, is therefore the center of a system bearing a certain resemblance to the solar system. These systems are sometimes designated by names derived from those of their central bodies. Thus we have the Martian System, composed of Mars and its two satellites; the Jovian System, composed of Jupiter and its nine satellites; the Saturnian System, comprising the planet Saturn, its rings, and nine satellites.

A fourth class of bodies consists of the *comets*. These move round the sun generally in very eccentric orbits. We see them only on their approach to the sun, which, in the case of most of these bodies, occurs only at intervals of centuries, or even thousands of years. Even then a comet may fail to be seen unless under favorable conditions.

Besides the preceding bodies we have a countless number of meteoric particles revolving round the sun in regular orbits. These are probably related in some way to the comets. They are completely invisible except as they strike our atmosphere, when we see them as shooting stars.

The following is the arrangement of the planets in the order of their distance from the sun and with the number of satellites of each:

I. Inner Group of Major Planets:
    Mercury.
    Venus.

Earth, with one satellite.
Mars, with two satellites.

II. Group of Minor Planets, or Asteroids.

III. Outer Group of Major Planets:
Jupiter, with nine satellites.
Saturn, with nine satellites.
Uranus, with four satellites.
Neptune, with one satellite.
Pluto.

Instead of taking up these bodies in the order of their distance from the sun, we shall, after describing the sun, pass over Mercury and Venus to consider the earth and moon. Then we shall return to the other planets and describe them in order.

II

THE SUN

THE great central body of the solar system is naturally the first to claim our attention. We see that the sun is a shining globe. The first questions to present themselves to us are about the size and distance of this globe. It is easy to state its size when we know its distance. We know by measurement that the angle subtended by the sun's diameter is about half a degree. If we draw two lines making this angle with each other, and continue them indefinitely through the celestial spaces, the diameter of the sun must be equal to the separation of the lines at the distance of the sun. The exact determination is a very simple problem of trigonometry. It will suffice at present to say that the angle of 32' which the sun's diameter subtends to our eye shows that the distance of the sun is about 107.5 times its diameter in miles. If, then, we know the distance of the sun, we have only to divide it by 107.5 to get the sun's diameter.

Now the sun's mean distance from the earth is 92,-870,000 miles. Dividing by 107.5, we find the diameter to be about 864,000 miles. This is about one hundred and ten times the diameter of the earth. It follows that the volume of the sun is more than one million three hundred thousand times that of the earth.

The sun's average density is only one fourth that of

the earth, and about four tenths greater than that of water.

Its mass is about 332,000 times that of the earth.

Gravity at the sun's surface is 28 times that at the surface of the earth. If it were possible for a human being to be placed there, an ordinary man would weigh two tons and be crushed by his own weight.

The sun's importance to us arises from its being our great source of heat and light. Were these withdrawn, not only would the world be enveloped in unending night, but, in the course of a short time, in eternal frost. We all know that during a clear night the surface of the earth grows colder through the radiation into space of the heat received from the sun during the day. Without the daily influx, the loss of heat would go on until the cold around us would far exceed that which we now experience in the polar regions. Vegetation would be impossible. The oceans would freeze over, and all life on the earth would soon be extinct.

The surface of the sun which we ordinarily see is called the *photosphere*. This term is used to distinguish the visible surface from the more nearly transparent layers above it, and the vast invisible interior of the sun. To the naked eye, the photosphere looks entirely uniform. But through a telescope we see that the whole surface has a mottled appearance, which has been aptly compared to that of a plate of rice soup. Examination under the best conditions shows that this appearance is due to minute and very irregular grains which are scattered all over the photosphere.

When we compare the brightness of different regions of the photosphere, we find that the apparent center of

the disk is brighter than the edge. The difference can be seen even without a telescope, if we look at the sun through a dark glass, or when it is setting in a dense haze. The falling off in the light is especially rapid as we approach the extreme edge of the disk, where it is little more than half as bright as at the center. There is also a difference of color, the light of the edge having a lurid appearance as compared with that of the center.

The photosphere is the limiting level of the sun below which we cannot see. Although it seems as sharply defined as the surface of a ball, it has scarcely more than a ten thousandth of the density of the air around us. We view this level through many thousands of miles of the much less dense material which constitutes the sun's "atmosphere." The darkening and reddening of the photosphere near the edge of the disk is caused not so much by the interposition of a greater thickness of this atmosphere as by the smaller depth of the photosphere in this region. Our oblique view of the edge of the sun is cut off at a higher and cooler level, where the light is less intense and redder.

ROTATION OF THE SUN

Careful observations show that the sun, like the earth, rotates from west to east on an axis passing through its center. Using the same terms as in the case of the earth, we call the points in which the axis intersects the surface the *poles* of the sun, and the circle around it halfway between the poles the sun's *equator*. The period of rotation at the equator is 24.7 days. As the

distance around the sun is more than one hundred and ten times that round the earth, the speed of rotation must be more than four times that of the earth's rotation to make it complete the circuit in the time that it does. At the sun's equator the speed is more than a mile a second.

An interesting feature of this rotation is that it is completed in longer periods with increasing distance from the equator. Near the sun's north and south poles, the period of the rotation is as much as 34 days. Were the sun a solid body, like the earth, all its parts would have to rotate at the same time. Hence the sun is not a solid body, but must be either liquid or gaseous, at least at its surface.

The equator of the sun is inclined seven degrees to the plane of the earth's orbit. Its direction is such that in our spring months the north pole is turned seven degrees away from us, and the central point of the apparent disk is about that amount south of the sun's equator. In our summer and autumn months this is reversed.

SPOTS ON THE SUN

When the sun is examined with a telescope, dark spots will generally, though not always, be seen on its surface. These are carried around by the rotation of the sun, and it is by means of them that the period of rotation is most easily determined. A spot which appears at the center of the desk will, in six days, be carried to the western edge, and will there disappear. At the end of about two weeks, if the spot survives, it will reappear at the eastern edge.

Part III

THE SUN, EARTH, AND MOON

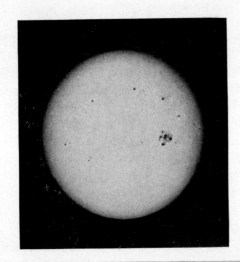

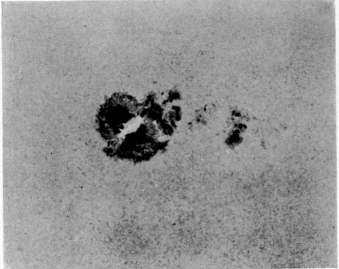

FIG. 13.—(above) *The Spotted Disk of the Sun.*
(below) *A large Sun-spot.* (*From photographs at Yerkes Observatory.*)

The spots have a wide range in size, from minute points, barely visible in a good telescope, to those that are large enough to be seen with the naked eye through a dark glass. Ordinarily, they appear in groups, and a group may sometimes be discerned with the naked eye when the individual spots cannot be seen. Single spots have measured as much as 50,000 miles in diameter. The largest groups have extended over one sixth of the disk.

As a group of spots develops, it spreads along a circle parallel to the sun's equator. The leader spot, in the direction of the sun's rotation, is likely to be the largest of the group, and the longest lived, remaining for some time after the others have vanished. Single spots are usually the survivors of groups. The spot which brings up the rear of the group is often of very large size also. The normal spot is nearly circular, having a darker central part, the umbra, and a lighter border, the penumbra. In the process of disintegration the spots break into very irregular fragments.

It has been established by nearly three centuries of observation of sun-spots that the frequency varies with some regularity in the average period of about eleven years. In some years, few spots, or perhaps none at all, can be seen at any one time. This was the case in 1912 and again in 1923. The year following, a slightly greater number show themselves; and they increase year after year for about five years, on the average. Then the frequency begins to diminish, year after year, until the cycle is completed, and the increase begins again. These mutations have been traced back to the time of

Galileo, although it was not until 1843 that Schwabe's observations established their periodicity.

The most recent maximum of sun-spots occurred in the spring of 1928. The spots will be most numerous again about 1939.

The periodic variation in the numbers of sun-spots is one manifestation of a more general eleven-year cycle in which many solar and terrestrial phenomena are included. The scarlet prominences are more frequent near the times of sun-spot maxima. The sun's corona changes form as the spots increase and diminish. The output of the sun's radiation varies in this cycle also. Magnetic storms on the earth—occasions when the compass needle gyrates in an erratic way, and when communication by wire and radio becomes difficult— increase in number and intensity with the spots. Displays of the aurora, or "northern lights," are more frequent and spectacular when sun-spots are numerous. Slight variations of weather conditions in this cycle seem to be established.

Another noteworthy law connected with the sun's spots is that they are not found all over the sun, but only in certain regions of solar latitude. They are rather rare on the sun's equator, but become more frequent as we go north or south of the equator till we get to fifteen degrees of latitude, north or south. From this region to twenty degrees the frequency is greatest; then it falls off, so that beyond thirty degrees a spot is rarely seen. These regions are shown in Figure 14, where the shading is darker the more frequent the spots. If we let a white globe represent the sun, and indicate by a black dot on it the location of every spot observed during a number of years, the dotting would make the globe look as represented in the figure.

Groups of numerous small spots brighter than the photosphere in general are usually to be seen on the

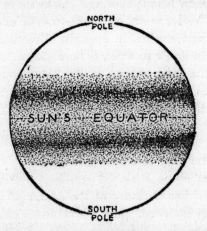

FIG. 14.   *Frequency of Sun-spots in Different Latitudes on the Sun*

sun, and most often in the neighborhoods of spots. These are the *faculæ*.

Sun-spots are manifestations of great whirling storms in the sun. They bear considerable resemblance to our own cyclones and tornadoes, except that they are on a vaster scale. The very hot gases move upward in the solar vortex. On reaching the photosphere, where the pressure is much less than in the regions below, the gases spread, flowing out over the surface. By this expansion they are cooled and become less luminous therefore. Thus the dark spot. This flat top of the mushroom-shaped vortex is still very hot and bright.

It appears dark simply by contrast with the surrounding undisturbed surface of the sun.

Just as terrestrial cyclones, in consequence of the earth's rotation, spin in the counter clockwise direction in the northern hemisphere and clockwise in the southern, so the leader spots of groups north and south of the solar equator whirl in opposite directions. The influence of the sun's rotation is here shown. But the behavior of the solar storms is the more complex. The follower spot of the group is likely to turn in the contrary direction to the leader, while other spots of the group may take either direction. A very surprising feature is that the directions of the solar vortices are reversed after each sun-spot minimum.

The gases above the dark sun-spot are sucked into the region of low pressure at the center of the vortex. And as they descend, they whirl also. This effect is clearly exhibited in the photographs with the spectroheliograph, a special instrument which is accountable for much of the present knowledge of solar phenomena.

Forty years ago, Hale in America and Deslandres in France independently invented the spectroheliograph. It is an attachment to the telescope by means of which the sun may be photographed in the light of a single chemical element, for example, calcium or hydrogen. When the instrument is set for hydrogen, the photograph shows only that part of the sun that is hydrogen —the *flocculi*, or masses of this gas. Their arrangement in the vicinity of a sun-spot reveals the vortex overlying the spot. With this instrument it is possible to photograph the solar prominences, the flame-like projections from the edge of the sun, without waiting for a total solar eclipse. Many of the solar phenomena which are depicted by the spectroheliograph can now be viewed directly with the spectrohelioscope, recently invented by Hale, and now employed at a number of observatories in various parts of the world.

THE PROMINENCES AND CHROMOSPHERE

The next remarkable feature of the sun to be described consists in the prominences. Our knowledge of these objects has an interesting history, which will be mentioned in describing eclipses of the sun. The prominences are large masses of highly rarefied, glowing gas, projecting from every part of the sun. They are of such extent that the earth, if immersed in them, would be as a grain of sand in the flame of a candle. They rise with enormous velocity, sometimes hundreds of miles a second. Like the faculæ, they are more numerous in the sun-spot zones, but are not confined to those zones. The glare around the sun caused by the reflection of light by the air around us renders them entirely invisible to ordinary vision, even with the telescope, except when, during total eclipses of the sun, the glare is cut off by the intervention of the moon. They may then be seen, even with the naked eye, as scarlet projections, as if from the black disc of the moon.

The prominences have two forms, the eruptive and the quiescent. The first rise from the sun like immense sheets of flame; the latter seem to be at rest above it, like clouds floating in the air. We cannot certainly say what supports them. Very likely, however, it is a repulsive force of the sun's rays.

Spectrum analysis shows that these prominences are composed of hydrogen, calcium, and other gases. It is to the hydrogen that they owe their red color. Continued study of the prominences shows them to be connected with a thin layer of gases which surrounds and rests upon the photosphere. This layer is called the *chromosphere*, from its deep red color, similar to that of the prominences. As in the case of the latter, its lurid light is that of hydrogen; but it contains calcium and other elements as well.

The outermost appendage of the sun to be considered is the *corona*. This is seen only during total eclipses as a soft effulgence surrounding the sun, and extending from it in long rays, sometimes exceeding the diameter of the sun in length. Its exact nature is still in doubt. It will be described in the chapter on eclipses.

THE SUN'S CONSTITUTION

Let us now recapitulate what makes up the sun as we see and know it.

We have first the vast interior of the globe which, of course, we can never see.

What we see when we look at the sun is the shining surface of this globe, the photosphere. It is not a real surface, but more likely a gaseous layer several hundred miles deep which we cannot distinguish from a surface. This layer is variegated by spots, and in or over it rise the faculæ.

On the top of the photosphere rests the layer of gases called the chromosphere, which can be observed at any time with a powerful spectroscope, but can be seen by direct vision only during total eclipses.

From the red chromosphere project the equally red flames called the prominences.

Surrounding the whole is the corona.

Such is the sun as we see it. What can we say about what it really is? First, is it solid, liquid, or gaseous?

That the visible surface is not solid is shown by the character of the rotation. Different parts of the surface rotate in different periods, as we have seen. Moreover, the high temperature suggests that it cannot be either solid or liquid. For many years it has been believed also that the interior of the sun must be a mass of gas, compressed to the density of a liquid by the enormous pressure of its superincumbent portions.

Everyone will agree that the sun must be hot. To produce the warmth of a midsummer day, at the distance of more than ninety million miles, the sun must be very hot indeed. And this is certainly true, as the appropriate measurements show. The photosphere, which is the immediate source of the sun's radiation, has a temperature of six thousand degrees Centigrade, or more than ten thousand degrees Fahrenheit.

The different ways of determining the sun's temperature, all of which give about the same result, depend on accepted relations between the temperature of a radiator and the quantity or quality of its radiation. For example, the rate of radiation is proportional to the fourth power of the temperature. This is known as Stefan's law. It informs us that if the temperature of a radiator is doubled, the rate at which it radiates becomes sixteen times as great as before.

Let a flat-bottomed basin be filled with cool water to the depth of two fifths of an inch, and exposed to the vertical rays of the sun. At the end of a minute, a thermometer would register a rise in the temperature of the water, which would amount to three and a half degrees Fahrenheit, if there were no air intervening, and no leakage of heat from the water meanwhile.

It follows that a spherical shell of cool water two fifths of an inch thick, having a radius equal to the earth's distance from the sun and the sun in the center, would be warmed by this amount in a minute. Since the shell completely encloses the sun, we have caught in this way the sun's total radiation in a minute, and have measured its effect.

By such measurements it is found that energy to the amount of 70,000 horsepower is streaming continually from every square yard of the sun's surface. And from results such as this the temperature of the sun can be calculated by means of the radiation laws. In practice, a very delicate instrument, the pyrheliometer, is employed instead of the basin of water and the thermometer. Observations with this instrument have been made for many years at the various stations of the Smithsonian Astrophysical Observatory.

Since we cannot look below the photosphere into the sun's interior, it is not the easiest matter to form a clear idea of the conditions there. We may well suppose that the pressure and temperature both increase with increasing depth. As early as 1870, the American physicist Lane calculated internal temperatures of the sun on the assumption that there is a state of equilibrium everywhere within. At every point the weight of the overlying layers is perfectly supported by the expansive force of the heated gases. The problem then consists in calculating how hot the interior must be in order to prevent the collapse of the sun under its own weight.

In recent years the theoretical studies of the interiors of the sun and the other stars have been pursued with especial vigor by Eddington, Jeans, and Milne in England. Eddington finds at the sun's center a density fifty times that of water, and a temperature of thirty or forty million degrees Centigrade. Milne gives enormously greater figures for the central density and temperature. The problem is not yet completely solved.

THE SOURCE OF THE SUN'S HEAT

From every square yard in its surface the sun pours forth energy equivalent to 70,000 horsepower. Knowing that the sun's diameter is 864,000 miles we can easily calculate the number of square yards in its surface. On multiplying this number by 70,000 we have the enormous number which expresses in horsepower the total amount of energy continually issuing from the sun. When we recall that the sun has been shining with something like its present intensity for thousands of millions of years, as geologists and biologists assure us that it has, we find ourselves confronted by an important and difficult question.

What is the source of all this radiant energy? It comes, of course, immediately from the photosphere. But new supplies of energy must be passed up continually to the photosphere to make possible the continual radiation. What, then, is the source of the apparently inexhaustible supply in the interior, that keeps the sun shining day after day for millions upon millions of years?

Now the law of the conservation of energy asserts that energy cannot emerge from nothing. It can be transformed from one type to another, but the total amount of energy in the universe cannot increase. Unless the sun continually receives energy from without, its supply must be diminishing at the enormous rate that we have noticed. It might well be supposed that the supply will some day be entirely dissipated, that the sun will grow dim and finally cease to shine. But the sun shines on, century after century, with apparently undiminished splendor. How can this be?

It must not be imagined that the sun is simply cooling from an originally still hotter state. Nor can the sunshine be properly ascribed to combustion within the sun. Such processes would be concluded much too soon. In addition, the sun is certainly too hot to burn. The idea that the continual falling of great numbers of meteors into the sun may increase its supply of energy enough to offset the loss by radiation is not consistent with the facts. The numbers of meteors drawn into the sun are insufficient to keep up the supply of energy. Moreover, such delivery of energy at the sun's surface could have little effect on the interior; it is there that the high temperature must be maintained in order to prevent the collapse of the sun.

Three quarters of a century ago, the physicist Helmholtz set forth the contraction theory of the sun's heat, which for many years afterward enjoyed the confidence of scientists. He showed that a shrinkage of 140 feet yearly in the sun's radius would produce as much heat as the sun loses annually in consequence of its radiation. According to this theory, the sun was formerly larger and more tenuous. This view is consistent with the nebular hypothesis of Laplace, generally approved in Helmholtz's time, which supposed that the sun and its system developed by the shrinking of an originally rarefied mass of gas. In the future, according to the contraction theory, the sun will become so compact that it cannot continue to shrink fast enough to offset the loss of heat by radiation. In a few million years it would be too cool to promote life on the earth.

The contraction theory pictured a gloomy prospect, the end of the world of living beings within a brief interval—brief astronomically, at least. But in recent years, the contraction theory has met with disapproval, along with the hypothesis of Laplace. In shrinking to its present size from dimensions as large as we please, the sun has gained enough heat to keep it shining at the present rate for scarcely more than twenty million years. It has certainly been shining at this rate for a vastly longer time. Thus the contraction theory fails to account for the maintenance of the sun's radiation in the past. We have no greater confidence in its prediction for the future. There is, in fact, no certain evidence that the sun is contracting progressively at all.

With the discovery of radioactivity, astronomers inquired as to whether the sun's long-continued radiation might not be kept up by the disintegration of radium and similar elements in its interior. Appropriate calculations soon gave the negative answer. A way is left open, however, if we wish to imagine that the sun contains radioactive elements more complex than the heaviest element, uranium, found in the earth. It should be added that we have no knowledge of such super-radioactive elements.

The quest of the correct solution of the problem continues. It is to-day one of the fundamental problems of physical science. Evidently it concerns not the sun alone, but all the stars as well. It is now suggested that the source of the sun's radiation is within the atoms— that much of the sun's mass is convertible, and is in fact continually being converted into energy to keep the sun shining. If this is really the source we are seeking, then the sun must be losing mass at a prodigious rate; during every four minutes the mass of the sun must be reduced a thousand million tons.

III

THE EARTH

THE globe on which we live, being one of the planets, would be entitled to a place among the heavenly bodies even if it had no other claims on our attention. Insignificant though it is in size when compared with the great bodies of the universe, or even with the four giant planets of our system, it is the largest of the group to which it belongs. Of the rank which it might claim as the abode of man we need not speak.

What is the earth? We may describe it in the most comprehensive way as a globe of matter nearly eight thousand miles in diameter, bound together by the mutual gravitation of its parts. We all know that it is not exactly spherical, but bulges out very slightly at the equator. The problem of determining its exact shape and size is made more difficult by the surface irregularities. Then too, there is no very precise way of measuring distances across the great oceans or of extending the measurements into the polar regions. The size and shape must be determined principally from the measures across or along the continents. Owing to the importance of such work, the leading nations have from time to time entered into it. The United States Coast and Geodetic Survey has completed the measurement of a line of triangles extending from the Atlantic to the Pacific oceans. North and south measurements both on the Atlantic and Pacific coasts have been executed. The English have made measures of the same sort in Africa, and the Russians and Germans on their respective territories.

The latest conclusions concerning the form and size of the earth may be summed up thus. We remark in the first place that by the figure of the earth geodetists do not mean the figure of the continents, but of the ocean level as it would be if canals admitting the water of the oceans were dug through the continents. The earth thus defined is approximately an ellipsoid, of which the smaller diameter is that through the poles, and which has about the following dimensions:

> Polar diameter, 7,900.0 miles.
> Equatorial " 7,926.7 miles.

It will be seen that the equatorial diameter is 26.7 miles greater than the polar.

THE EARTH'S INTERIOR

What we know of the earth by direct observation is confined almost entirely to its surface. The greatest depth to which man has ever been able to penetrate compares with the size of the globe only as the skin of an apple does to the body of the fruit itself.

I shall first invite the reader's attention to some facts about weight, pressure, and gravity in the earth. Let us consider a cubic foot of soil forming part of the outer surface of the earth. This upper cubic foot presses upon its bottom with its own weight, perhaps one hundred and fifty pounds. The cubic foot below it weighs an equal amount, and therefore presses on its bottom with a force equal to its own weight with the weight of the other foot added to it. This continual increase of pressure goes on as we descend. Every square foot in the earth's interior sustains a pressure equal to the weight of a column of the earth a foot square extending to the surface. Not many yards below the surface this pressure will be measured in tons; at the depth of a mile it may be thirty or forty tons; at the depth of one hundred miles, thousands of tons; continually increasing to the center. Under this enormous pressure the matter composing the inner portion of the earth is highly compressed. It is heavier material also. The mean density of the earth is known to be five and one half times that of water, while the superficial density is only two or three times that of water.

One of the well-established facts about the earth is that the temperature continually increases as we penetrate below the surface in deep mines. The rate of increase is different in different latitudes and regions. The average increase is one degree Fahrenheit for a descent of fifty or sixty feet.

How far toward the earth's center does this increase of temperature extend? In answer to this question we can say that the effect cannot be merely superficial, because, in that case, the exterior portions would have cooled off long ago, so that we should have no considerable increase of heat as we descend. The fact that the heat has been kept up during the whole of the earth's existence shows that it must still be very intense toward the center, and that the rate of increase near the surface must go on for many miles into the interior.

At this rate of increase the material of the earth would be red hot at a depth of ten or fifteen miles, while at one or two hundred miles the heat would be sufficient to melt all the substances which form the earth's crust. This fact suggested to geologists of earlier times the idea that our globe is really a molten mass, like a mass of melted iron, covered by a cool crust a few miles thick, on which we dwell. The existence of volcanoes and the occurrence of earthquakes seemed to give additional weight to this view.

But in recent years the astronomer and physicist have collected evidence, which is as conclusive as such evidence can be, that the earth is solid from center to surface, and even more rigid than a similar mass of steel. The subject was first developed most fully by Lord Kelvin, who showed that, if the earth were a fluid, surrounded by a crust, the action of the moon would not cause tides in the ocean, but would merely tend to stretch out the entire earth in the direction of the moon, leaving the relative positions of the crust and the water unchanged.

Equally conclusive is the curious phenomenon which we shall describe presently of the variation of latitudes on the earth's surface. Not only a globe of which the interior is soft, but even a globe no more rigid than steel could not rotate as the earth does.

How, then, are we to reconcile the enormous temperature and the solidity? There seems to be only one solution possible. The matter of the interior of the earth is kept solid by the enormous pressure. It is found experimentally that when samples of rocks are raised to the melting point, and then subjected to heavy pressure, the effect of the pressure is to make them solid again. Thus, as we increase the temperature we have only to increase the pressure also to keep the material of the earth solid. And thus it is that, as we descend into the earth, the increase of pressure more than keeps pace with the rise of temperature and thus keeps the whole mass solid.

GRAVITY AND DENSITY OF THE EARTH

Another interesting question connected with the earth is that of its density, or specific gravity. We all know that a lump of lead is heavier than a lump of iron of equal volume, while the latter is heavier than a piece of wood of the same size. Is there any way of determining what a cubic foot of earth would weigh if taken out from a great depth of its vast interior? If there is, then we can determine what the actual weight of the whole earth is. The solution depends on the gravitation of matter.

Every child is familiar with the effect of gravitation from the time it begins to walk, but the profoundest philosopher knows nothing of its cause. According to Newton's theory of gravitation, the force by which all bodies on the surface of the earth are urged toward its center does not reside merely in the center of the earth, but is exerted by every particle of matter composing our globe. Newton extended his theory yet farther by the statement that every particle of matter in the universe attracts every other particle with a force that diminishes as the square of the distance increases. This means that at twice the distance the attraction will be divided by four; at three times, by nine; at four times, by sixteen, and so on.

Granting this, it follows that all objects around us have their own gravitating power, and the question arises: Can we show this power by experiment and measure its amount? The mathematical theory shows that globes of equal density attract small bodies at their surfaces with a force proportioned to their diameter. A globe two feet in diameter, of the same density as the earth, should attract with a force one twenty-millionth of the earth's gravity.

Physicists have succeeded in measuring the attraction of globes of lead and other materials having a diameter of a foot, more or less. This measurement is delicate and difficult, and its accuracy would have seemed incredible a few years ago. The apparatus used is, in its principle, of the simplest kind. A very light horizontal rod is suspended at its center by a thread of the finest and most flexible material that can be obtained. This rod is balanced by having a small ball attached to each end. What is measured is the attraction of the globes of lead upon these two balls. The former are placed in such a position as to unite their attraction in giving the rod a slight twisting motion in the horizontal plane. To appreciate the difficulties of the case, we must call to mind that the attraction may not amount to the ten-millionth part of the weight of the little balls. It would be difficult to find any object so light that its weight would not exceed this force. Not only the weight of a mosquito but even of its finest limb exceeds the quantity which has been measured. If a mosquito were placed under a microscope an expert operator could cut off from one antenna a piece small enough to express the force measured.

Heyl's determination of the constant of gravitation, at the United States Bureau of Standards, is the most recent. The outcome of such measurements is that the mean density of the earth is slightly more than five and a half times that of water. This is a little less than the density of iron, but much more than that of any ordinary stone. As the mean density of the materials which compose the earth's crust is scarcely more than one half of this amount, it follows that near the center the matter composing the earth must be compressed to a density not only far exceeding that of iron, but probably that of lead.

VARIATION OF LATITUDE

We know that the earth rotates on an axis passing through the center and intersecting the earth's surface at either pole. If we imagine ourselves standing exactly on a pole of the earth, with a flagstaff fastened in the ground, we should be carried round the flagstaff by the earth's rotation once in twenty-four hours. We should become aware of the motion by seeing the sun and stars apparently moving in the opposite direction in horizontal circles by virtue of the diurnal motion. Now, the great discovery of the variation of latitude is this: The point in which the axis of rotation intersects the surface is not fixed, but moves around in a somewhat variable and irregular curve, contained within a circle nearly sixty feet in diameter. That is to say, if standing at the north pole we should observe its position day by

day, we should find it moving one, two, or three inches
every day, describing in the course of time a curve
around one central point, from which it would sometimes be farther away and sometimes nearer. It would
make a complete revolution in this irregular way in
about fourteen months.

How is this known? The answer is that by astronomical observations we can, on any night, determine
the exact angle between the plumb line at the place
where we stand and the axis on which the earth is rotating on that particular day. Four or five stations for
making these observations were established around the
earth in 1900 by the International Geodetic Association. One of these stations is near Gaithersburg, Md.,
another is on the Pacific coast, a third is in Japan, and
a fourth in Italy. Before these were established,
observations having the same object were made in various parts of Europe and America.

The variation which we have described was originally
demonstrated by Küstner in Germany, in 1888, by
means of a great mass of astronomical observations
not made for this special purpose. Since then investigation has been going on with the view of determining
the exact curve described. What has been shown thus
far is that the variation is much wider some years than
others. It appears that in the course of seven years
there will be one in which the pole describes the greater
part of a comparatively wide circle, while three or four
years later it will for several months scarcely move from
its central position.

If the earth were composed of a fluid, or even of a
substance which would bend no more than the hardest

steel, such a motion of the axis as this would be impossible. Our globe must therefore, in the general average, be more rigid than steel.

THE ATMOSPHERE

The atmosphere is astronomically, as well as physically, a most important appendage of the earth. Necessary though it is to our life, it constitutes one of the greatest obstructions with which the astronomer has to deal. It absorbs more or less of all the light that passes through it, and thus slightly changes the color of the heavenly objects as we see them and renders them somewhat dimmer, even in the clearest sky. It also refracts the light passing through it, causing it to describe a slightly curved line, concave toward the earth, instead of passing straight to the astronomer's eye. The result is that the stars appear slightly higher above the horizon than they actually are. The light coming directly down from a star in the zenith suffers no refraction. The latter increases as the star is farther from the zenith, but even forty-five degrees away it is only one minute of arc, less than the smallest amount that the unaided eye can plainly perceive; yet this is a very important quantity to the astronomer. The nearer the object is to the horizon, the greater the rate at which the refraction increases; twenty-eight degrees above the horizon it is about twice as great as at forty-five degrees; at the horizon the apparent elevation of the celestial body by refraction is more than one half a degree, that is more than the whole diameter of the sun or moon. The result is that when we see the sun just

about to touch the horizon at sunset or sunrise its whole
disk is in reality below the horizon. We see it only in
consequence of the refraction of its light. Another result of the rapid increase near the horizon is that, in
this position, the sun looks decidedly flattened to the
eye, its vertical diameter being shorter than the horizontal one. Anyone may notice this who has an opportunity to look at the sun as it is setting in the ocean.
It arises from the fact that the lower edge of the sun
is refracted more than the upper edge.

When the sun sets in the ocean in the clear air of the
tropics a beautiful effect may be noticed, which can
rarely or never be seen in the thicker air of our latitudes. It arises from the unequal refraction of the rays
of light by the atmosphere. Like a prism of glass the
atmosphere refracts the red rays the least and the successive spectral colors, yellow, green, blue, and violet,
more and more. The blue and violet light from the setting sun is largely scattered by the atmosphere before
reaching us. The result is that, as the edge of the sun
is disappearing in the ocean, these successive rays are
lost sight of in the same order. Two or three seconds
before the sun has disappeared, the little spark of its
limb which still remains visible is seen to change color
and rapidly grow paler. The last glimpse which we see
is that of a disappearing flash of green light.

IV

THE MOON

VARIOUS measurements agree in placing the moon at an average distance of a little less than 240,000 miles. This distance is obtained by direct measure of the parallax, as will be explained hereafter, and also by calculating how far off the moon must be in order that, being projected into space, it may describe an orbit around the earth in the time that it actually does perform its revolution. The orbit is elliptic, so that the actual distance varies. Sometimes it is ten or fifteen thousand miles less, at other times as much more, than the average.

The diameter of the moon's globe is a little more than one fourth that of the earth; more exactly, it is 2,160 miles. The most careful measures show no deviation from the globular form except that the surface is very irregular.

REVOLUTION AND PHASES OF THE MOON

The moon accompanies the earth in its revolution round the sun. To some the combination of the two motions seems a little complex; but it need not offer any real difficulty. Imagine a chair standing in the center of a railway car in rapid motion, while a person is walking around it at a distance of three feet. He can go round and round without varying his distance from the chair and without any difficulty arising from the motion of the car. Thus the earth moves forward in its orbit,

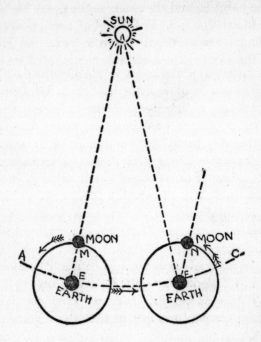

Fig. 15.   *Revolution of the Moon Round the Earth*

and the moon continually revolves around it without greatly varying its distance from us.

The actual time of the moon's revolution around the earth is twenty-seven days eight hours; but the time from one new moon to another is twenty-nine days thirteen hours. The difference arises from the earth's motion around the sun; or, which amounts to the same thing, the apparent motion of the sun along the ecliptic. To show this, let AC be a small arc of the earth's orbit around the sun. Suppose that at a certain time the earth is at the point E, and the moon at the point M, between the earth and the sun. At the end of twenty-seven days eight hours the earth will have moved from E to F. While the earth is making this motion the moon will have moved around the orbit in the direction of the arrows, so as to have reached the point N. At the moment when the lines EM and FN are parallel to each other, the moon will have completed its actual revolution and will seem to be in the same place among the stars as before. But the sun is now in the direction FS. The moon therefore has to continue its motion before it catches up to the sun. This requires a little more than two days, and makes the whole time between two new moons twenty-nine and a half days.

The varying phases of the moon depend upon its position with respect to the sun. Since it is an opaque globe, without light of its own, we see it only as the light of the sun illuminates it. When it is between us and the sun its dark hemisphere is turned toward us, and it is entirely invisible. The time of this position in the almanacs is called "new moon," but we cannot commonly see the moon for nearly two days after this time, because it is lost in the bright twilight of evening. On the second and third day, however, we see a small portion of the illuminated globe, having the familiar form of a thin crescent. This crescent is sometimes called the new moon, although the time given in the almanac is several days earlier.

In this position, and for several days longer, we may

see the entire face of the moon, the dark parts shining with a faint gray light, which is reflected from the earth to the moon. An inhabitant of the moon, if there were such, would then see the earth in his sky like a nearly full moon, although this would be larger than the moon appears to us. As the moon advances in its orbit day after day, this earthlight diminishes, and about the time of first quarter disappears from our sight, owing to the brightness of the illuminated portion of the moon, and to the reduced light of the earth, then at the quarter phase also.

Seven or eight days after the almanac time of new moon, the moon reaches its first quarter. We then see half of the illuminated disk. During the week following, the moon has the form called gibbous. At the end of the second week the moon is opposite the sun, and we see its entire hemisphere like a round disk. This we call full moon. During the remainder of its course the phases recur in reverse order, as we all know.

We might regard all these recurrences as too well known to need description, yet, in "The Ancient Mariner," a star is described as seen between the two horns of the moon as though there were no dark body there to intercept our view of the star. Probably more than one poet has described the new moon as seen in the eastern sky, or the evening full moon as seen in the west.

THE SURFACE OF THE MOON

We can see with the naked eye that the moon's surface is variegated by bright and dark regions. The latter are sometimes conceived to have a vague resemblance to the human face, the nose and eyes being especially prominent. Hence the "man in the moon." Through even the smallest telescopes we see that the surface has an immense variety of detail; and the more powerful the telescope the more details we see. The first thing to strike us on a telescopic examination will be the elevations, or mountains, as they are commonly called. These are best seen about the time of the quarter phase, when the long shadows near the sunrise or sunset line displays the irregularities in sharp relief. At full moon they cannot be so well made out, because the sun is shining more nearly straight down, and everything is illuminated. Although these elevations and depressions are called mountains they are different in form, for the most part, from the ordinary mountains of the earth. There is a closer resemblance between them and the craters of our great volcanoes. A very common form is that of a circular fort, often many miles in diameter, with walls which may be thousands of feet high, and a fairly level floor within. In many of the lunar craters one or more peaks rise abruptly from the center of the floor. At first quarter we can see the shadow of the walls and central peaks cast upon the interior flat surface. The higher power the more details we shall see. Just what these consist of it is impossible to say; they may be solid rock or they may be piles of loose stone. As we can see no object on the moon, even with the most powerful telescope, unless it is more than a hundred feet in diameter, we cannot say what the exact nature of the surface is in its minutest portions.

The early observers with the telescope supposed that the dark portions were seas and the brighter portions

continents. This notion was founded on the fact that
the darker portions looked smoother than the others.
Names were therefore given to these supposed oceans,
such as *Mare Imbrium*, the Sea of Storms; *Mare
Serenitatis*, the Sea of Calms, etc. These names, fanci-
ful though they be, are still retained to designate the
large dark regions on the moon. A very slight improvement in the telescope, however, showed that the idea of
these dark regions being oceans was illusory. The difference of aspect arises from the lighter or darker
shade of the materials which compose the lunar surface.

One of the most remarkable features is the long
bright lines which radiate from certain points on the
moon. A very low telescopic power will show the most
conspicuous of these. In the vicinity of the south pole
of the moon, a point near the crater Tycho is the center of a fine system of bright rays. The appearance is
as if the moon had been cracked and the cracks filled
up with melted white matter. Whether we accept this
view or not, it is impossible to examine the surface of
the moon without the conviction that in some former
age it was the seat of great volcanic activity, which has
now ceased entirely.

A question often asked about the moon is whether
there is any air or water on its surface. To this the
answer of science is in the negative. Of course this does
not mean that there can absolutely not be a drop of
moisture nor the smallest trace of an atmosphere on
our satellite; all we can say is that if any atmosphere
surrounds the moon it is so rare that we have never
been able to get any evidence of its existence. If the

FIG. 16.—*Mountainous Surface of the Moon.*
(*From photograph at Yerkes Observatory.*)

moon had atmosphere of even one hundredth of the density of the earth's, its existence would be made known to us by refraction of the light from a star seen alongside the moon. But not the slightest trace of any such refraction can be discovered. If there is any water, it must be concealed in crevices, or diffused through the interior. Were there any large sheets of water in the equatorial regions they would reflect the light of the sun day by day, and would thus become clearly visible. The water would also evaporate during the long and hot lunar day, and would form an appreciable atmosphere if it were present in large quantities.

All this seems to settle another question; namely, that of the habitability of the moon. Life, in the form in which it exists on our earth, requires air and water for its support.

The total absence of air and water results in a state of things on the moon such as we never experience on the earth. So far as can be ascertained, not the slightest change ever takes place on its surface. A stone lying on the surface of the earth is continually attacked by the weather, and in the course of years is gradually disintegrated or washed away by the wind and water. But there is no weather on the moon, and a stone lying on its surface might rest there for unknown ages undisturbed by any cause whatever. The lunar surface is heated up intensely when the sun shines on it, and it becomes exceedingly cold when the sun has set. Except for these changes of temperature and the fall of meteors, there is absolutely nothing going on over the whole surface of the moon, so far as we can see. A world which has no weather and on which nothing ever happens—such is the moon.

ROTATION OF THE MOON

The rotation of the moon on its axis is the subject of so many questions that we shall explain it. Everyone knows that the moon always presents the same face to us. This shows that it rotates on its axis in the same period that it revolves around the earth. It might be supposed that it does not rotate at all. The confusion arises from the different ideas of motion. In physics we say that a body does not rotate, if a straight line passed through it, in any way except along the axis, always maintains the same direction. Now let us suppose such a line passed through the moon; then, if the latter did not rotate on its axis the rod would maintain its same direction while the moon, revolving around the earth, would appear at different points in its orbit, as we see it in Figure 17. A little study of this figure will show that as the moon revolves we should see every part of its surface in succession, unless it rotates on its axis.

HOW THE MOON PRODUCES TIDES

Those who live near the seashore are especially familiar with the rise and fall of the ocean which in the general average occurs about three quarters of an hour later every day, and which keeps pace with the apparent diurnal motion of the moon. That is to say, if it is high tide to-day when the moon is in a certain position in the heavens, it will be high tide when the moon is in or near that position day after day, month after month, and year after year. We know that the moon produces these tides by its attraction on the ocean. We readily understand that when the moon is above any region, its attraction raises the waters in that region; but the circumstance not so generally understood is

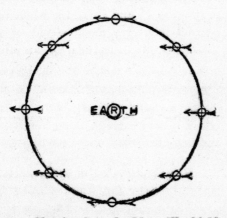

Fig. 17. *Showing how the Moon Would Move if It Did not Rotate on its Axis*

that there are two tides a day, high tide occurring not only under the moon, but on the side of the earth opposite the moon. The explanation is that the moon really attracts the earth itself as well as the water. If it attracted every part of the earth equally, the ocean included, there would then be no tides, and everything would go on the earth's surface as if there were no attraction at all. But as the attraction is as the inverse square of the distance, the moon attracts the regions of the earth and oceans which are nearest to it more than the average, and those that are farthest from it less than the average.

To show the effect of these changes let A, C, and H be three points on the earth attracted by the moon. Since the moon attracts C more than A, it pulls C away from A and thus increases the distance between A and C. At the same time pulling H more than C it increases the distance between H and C. If the whole earth were fluid, the attraction of the moon would be simply to draw this fluid out into the form of an ellipsoid, of

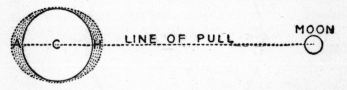

Fig. 18.   *How the Moon's Pull on the Earth and Ocean Produces Two Tides in a Day*

which the long diameter would be turned toward the moon. But since the earth is solid, it cannot be drawn out into this shape. But the ocean, being fluid, is thus drawn out. The result is that we have high tides at the two ends of the ellipsoid into which the ocean is drawn, and low tides in the mid-region.

The complete explanation of the subject requires a statement of the laws of motion which cannot be made here. I will, however, remark that if the attraction of the moon on the earth were always in the same direction, the two bodies would be drawn together in a few days. But owing to the revolution of the moon round the earth the direction of the pull is always changing,

so that in the course of a month the earth is drawn
only about three thousand miles from its mean position.

It might be supposed that if the moon produces the
tides in this way we should always have high tide when
the moon is on the meridian and low tide when the moon
is on the horizon. But such is not the case, for two reasons. In the first place, it takes time for the moon to
draw the waters out into the form of an ellipsoid, and
when it once gives them the motion necessary to keep
this form, that motion keeps up after the moon has
passed the meridian, just as a stone continues to rise
after it has left the hand or a wave goes forward by the
momentum of the water. The other cause is found in the
interruption of the motion by the great continents.
The tidal wave, as it is called, meeting a continent,
spreads out in one direction or the other, according to
the lay of the land, and may be a long time in passing
from one point to another. Thus arise all sorts of irregularities in the tides when we compare those in different places.

The sun produces tides as well as the moon, but
smaller ones. At the times of new and full moon the
two bodies unite their forces and cause the highest and
lowest tides. These are familiar to all dwellers on the
seacoast and are called *spring tides*. About the time of
the first and last quarters the attraction of the sun
opposes that of the moon and the tides do not rise so
high or fall so low, and these are called *neap tides*.

V

ECLIPSES OF THE MOON

AN ECLIPSE of the moon is caused by that body entering the shadow of the earth. An eclipse of the sun is caused by the moon passing between us and the sun. We shall explain the more interesting features of these phenomena and the laws of their recurrence.

Why is there not an eclipse of the moon at every full moon? The earth's shadow must always be in its place

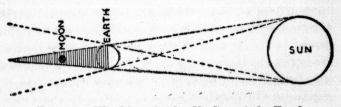

FIG. 19. *The Moon in the Shadow of the Earth*

opposite the sun; but the moon at the full phase commonly passes either above or below the shadow of the earth, and so fails to be eclipsed. This arises from the fact that the orbit of the moon has a small inclination, about five degrees, to the plane of the ecliptic, in which the earth moves, and in which the center of the shadow always lies. Returning to our former thought of the ecliptic being marked out on the celestial sphere, let us suppose that we also mark out the moon's apparent path among the stars during the course of its revolution. We should then find the orbit of the moon crossing that of the sun in two opposite points, at the very small angle of five degrees. These points of crossing are called *nodes*. At one node the moon passes from below, or south of the ecliptic, to the north of it. This is called the *ascending node*. At the other the moon passes from north to south of the ecliptic. This is called the *descending node*. The terms ascending and descending are applied to the node, because to us in the northern hemisphere, the north side of the ecliptic and equator seem to be above the south side.

At the points halfway between the nodes the center of the moon is above the ecliptic plane by about one twelfth its distance from us, that is, by about twenty thousand miles. Since the sun is larger than the earth, the shadow of the earth tapers gradually away from the earth. At the distance of the moon its diameter is about three fourths that of the earth, or about six thousand miles. Since its center is in the plane of the ecliptic, the shadow at the moon's distance extends only about three thousand miles above and below that plane. Hence the moon can pass through it only when it is near the nodes.

ECLIPSE SEASONS

The line joining the sun and moon of course turns round as the earth moves around the sun. It therefore crosses the moon's nodes twice in the course of a year. That is to say, if we suppose the nodes to be marked in the sky, the ascending node at one point, and the descending node at the opposite point, then the sun in its eastward movement along the ecliptic will appear to us to pass each of these points in the course of a year. While the sun is passing one node the shadow of the earth will seem to be passing the other. It is only near two times of the year, six months apart, that an eclipse of the sun or moon can occur. These *eclipse seasons* last about a month; that is to say, it is generally about a month from the time when the sun gets near enough to a node to allow of an eclipse until the time when it is too far past for an eclipse to occur. In 1930 the seasons were April and October.

If the moon's nodes were to keep the same positions on the ecliptic, eclipses could occur only in or near these two months. But, owing to the attraction of the sun on the earth and moon, the position of the nodes is continually changing in a direction opposite that of the motion of the two bodies. Each node makes a complete revolution westward around the celestial sphere in eighteen years and seven months. In this same period the eclipse seasons step backward around the whole year. On the average they occur about nineteen days earlier every year than they did the year before.

APPEARANCE OF ECLIPSED MOON

If we watch the moon when an eclipse is beginning, we shall see a small portion of its eastern edge gradually grow dim and finally disappear. As the moon advances, more and more of its face is darkened by entrance into the shadow. If, however, we look very carefully, we shall see that the part immersed in the shadow has not entirely disappeared, but shines with a very faint light. If the whole disk of the moon enters

into the shadow, the eclipse is said to be total; if only
a portion of the disk dips into the shadow, it is called
partial. When the eclipse is total, the light which almost always illuminates the eclipsed moon will be very
plainly seen, because it is not drowned out by the
dazzling light of the uneclipsed portion. This light, of
a dull red color, arises from the refraction of the
earth's atmosphere, which was described in a former
chapter. Those rays of the sun which just graze the
earth, or pass within a short distance of its surface,

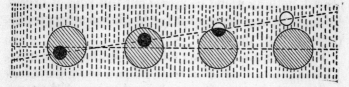

Fig. 20.   *Passage of the Moon through the Earth's
Shadow*

are thrown by refraction into the shadow, where they
fall on the moon. The red color is due to the same cause
that makes the sun appear red at sunset, namely, the
absorption of the green and blue rays by the atmosphere which lets the red rays pass.

Two or three eclipses of the moon occur every year;
of these one, at least, is nearly always total. But, of
course, the eclipse will be visible only in that hemisphere of the earth on which the moon is shining at the
time.

When the moon is eclipsed an observer on that body
would see an eclipse of the sun by the earth. The cause
of the phenomenon we have described would then be
plain enough to him. The apparent size of the earth

would be much larger than that of the moon as we see it. Its diameter would be between three and four times that of the sun. At first this immense body would be invisible when it approached the sun. What the observer would see would be the cutting off of the light of the sun by the advancing but invisible earth. When the latter had nearly covered the sun, its whole outline would be shown to him by a red light surrounding it, caused by the refraction of the earth's atmosphere. Finally, when the last trace of true sunlight had disappeared, nothing would be visible but this ring of bright red light having inside of it the black but otherwise invisible part of the earth.

The circumstances of an eclipse of the moon are quite different from those of a solar eclipse, to be described in the next chapter. It can always be seen at the same instant over the whole hemisphere of the earth on which the moon is shining at the time. A curious phenomenon occurs when the moon rises totally eclipsed. Then we may see it on one horizon, say the eastern one, while the sun is still visible on the western horizon. The explanation of this seeming paradox is that one of the two bodies is really below the horizon, but is so elevated by refraction that we can see it also.

ECLIPSES OF THE SUN

IF THE moon moved exactly in the plane of the ecliptic it would pass over the face of the sun at every new moon. But, owing to the inclination of its orbit, as described in the preceding chapter, it will actually do so only when the direction of the sun happens to be near one of the moon's nodes. When this occurs, we may see an eclipse of the sun, if we are on the right part of the earth.

Suppose that the moon passes over the sun. The first question is whether it can wholly hide the sun from our view. This depends not on the actual size of the two

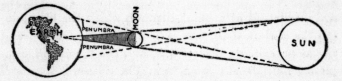

FIG. 21. *The Shadow of the Moon Thrown on the Earth during a Total Eclipse of the Sun*

bodies but on their apparent size. We know that the sun has about four hundred times the diameter of the moon. But it is also four hundred times as far from us as the moon. The curious result is that the two bodies appear to us of nearly the same size. Sometimes the moon appears a little larger, and sometimes slightly smaller. In the former case the moon may entirely hide the sun; in the latter case it cannot do so.

One important difference between an eclipse of the moon and of the sun is that the former has the same appearance wherever it is visible, while an eclipse of the sun depends upon the position of the observer. The most interesting eclipses are those in which the center of the moon passes exactly over that of the sun. These are called *central eclipses*. To see one, the observer must

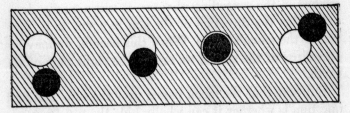

FIG. 22.   *The Moon Passing Centrally over the Sun during an Annular Eclipse*

station himself at a point through which the line joining the centers shall pass. Then if the apparent size of the moon exceeds that of the sun, the moon will completely hide the sun from view. The eclipse is then said to be *total*.

If the sun appears the larger, a ring of its light will surround the dark body of the moon at the moment of central eclipse. The latter is then called *annular* (Latin *annulus*, a ring).

The line of centers of the two bodies sweeps along the surface of the earth, and its course may be shown by a line marked on a map. Such maps, showing the regions and lines of eclipses, are published in advance in the nautical almanacs. An eclipse may be total or annular in a region a few miles north or south of this central line, but never for so far as one hundred miles. Outside this limit an observer will see only a partial eclipse, that is, one in which the moon partly covers the sun. In yet more distant regions of the earth there will be no eclipse at all.

BEAUTY OF A TOTAL ECLIPSE

A total eclipse is one of the most impressive sights that nature offers to the eye of man. To see it to the best advantage one should be in an elevated position commanding the widest possible view of the surrounding country, especially in the direction from which the shadow of the moon is to come. The first indication of anything unusual is to be seen, not on the earth or in the air, but on the disk of the sun. At the predicted moment a little notch will be seen to form somewhere on the western edge of the sun's outline. It increases minute by minute, gradually eating away, as it were, the visible sun. No wonder that imperfectly civilized people, when they saw the great luminary thus diminishing in size, fancied that a dragon was devouring its substance.

For some time, perhaps an hour, nothing will be noticed but the continued progress of the advancing moon. It will be interesting if, during this time, the observer is in the neighborhood of a tree that will permit the sun's rays to reach the ground through the small openings in its foliage. The little images of the sun which form here and there on the ground will then have the form of the partially eclipsed sun. Soon the sun appears as the crescent moon, but instead of increasing, the crescent form grows thinner minute by minute. Even then, so well has the eye accommodated itself to the diminishing light, there may be little noticeable darkness until the crescent has grown very thin. If the observer has a telescope with a dark glass for viewing the sun, he will now have an excellent opportunity of seeing the mountains on the moon. The unbroken limb of the sun will keep its usual soft and uniform outline. But the inside of the crescent, the edge of which is formed by the surface of the moon, will be rough and jagged in outline.

As the crescent is about to disappear, the advancing mountains on the rugged surface of the moon will reach the sun's edge, leaving nothing of the latter but a row of broken fragments or points of light, shining between the hollows on the lunar surface. They last but a second or two and then vanish.

Now is seen the glory of the spectacle. The sky is clear and the sun in mid-heaven, and yet no sun is visible. Where the latter ought to be the densely black globe of the moon hangs, as it were, in midair. It is surrounded by an effulgence radiating a saintly glory. This is the sun's *corona*, already mentioned in our chapter on the sun. Though bright enough to the unaided vision, it is seen to the best advantage with a telescope of very low magnifying power. Even a common opera glass may suffice. With a telescope of high power only a portion of the corona is visible, and thus the finest part of the effect is lost. A common spyglass, magnifying ten or twelve times, is better, so far as effect is concerned, than the largest telescope. Such an instrument will show not only the corona but the prominences also, the fantastic cloud-like forms of rosy color rising here and there, seemingly from the dark body of the moon.

ANCIENT ECLIPSES

It is remarkable that though the ancients were familiar with the fact of eclipses, and the more enlightened of them perfectly understood their causes, some even the laws of their recurrence, there are very few actual accounts of these phenomena in the writings of the ancient historians. The old Chinese annals now and then record the fact that an eclipse of the sun occurred at a certain time in some province or near some city of the empire. But no particulars are given. The Assyriologists have deciphered from ancient tablets a statement that an eclipse of the sun was seen at Nineveh, B. C. 763, June 15. Our astronomical tables show that there actually was a total eclipse of the sun on this day, during which the shadow passed a hundred miles or so north of Nineveh.

Perhaps the most celebrated of the ancient eclipses, and the one that has given rise to most discussion, is that known as the eclipse of Thales. Its principal historical basis is a statement of Herodotus that in a battle between the Lydians and the Medes the day was suddenly turned into night. The armies thereupon ceased battle and were more eager to come to terms with each other. It is added that Thales, the Milesian, had predicted to the Ionians this change of day into night, even the very year in which it should occur. Our astronomical tables show that there actually was a total eclipse of the sun in the year B. C. 585, which was near enough to the time of the battle to be the one alluded to, but it is now known that the path of the shadow did not quite reach the seat of hostilities till after sunset. Some doubt therefore still rests on the subject.

PREDICTION OF ECLIPSES

There is a law of the recurrence of eclipses which has been known from ancient times. It is based on the fact that the sun and moon return to nearly the same positions, relative to the node and perigee of the moon's orbit, after a period of six thousand five hundred and eighty-five days eight hours, or eighteen years and eleven days. This period is called the *Saros*. Eclipses of every sort repeat themselves at the end of a Saros. For example, the eclipse of May, 1900, may be regarded as a repetition of those which occurred in the years 1846, 1864, and 1882. But when such an eclipse recurs it is not visible in the same part of the earth, because of the excess of eight hours in the period. During this eight hours the earth performs one third of a rotation on its axis, which brings a different region under the sun. Each eclipse is visible in a region about one third of the way round the world, or one hundred and twenty degrees of longitude west of where it occurred before. Only after three periods will the recurrence be near the same region. But in the meantime the moon's line of motion will have changed so that the path of its shadow will pass farther north or south than before.

There are two series of solar eclipses remarkable for the long duration of the total phase. To one of these the eclipse of September 21, 1922, belongs. This will recur on October 1, 1940; it will be visible in South America. The duration of totality will be nearly six minutes.

To the other and yet more remarkable series belonged the eclipse of May 11, 1901. At the successive recurrences of this eclipse the duration of totality will be longer and longer through the twentieth century. In 1937, 1955, and 1973 it will exceed seven minutes. The maximum possible duration of total solar eclipse is seven minutes and a half.

THE SUN'S CORONA

The most spectacular feature of the total solar eclipse is the sun's corona, which can be seen only on these occasions. This pearly light around the sun comes abruptly into view at the beginning of totality and vanishes with equal abruptness at the ending. Photographs show the corona as a structure of intricate detail, changing form in a striking way as the numbers of sun-spots increase and diminish.

Near the time of sun-spot maximum, the corona has about the same extension in all directions from the sun. At this phase it has been likened to a dahlia. Petal-like forms project on all sides from the solar disk. Long streamers of faintly luminous stuff and elaborate arches above the red prominences are characteristic details also.

Around sun-spot minimum, short spikes emerge from the polar regions, curving toward the equator. They remind us of the pattern assumed by iron filings in the vicinity of a magnet. But studies of the polar streamers do not bear out the first impression of their close association with the sun's magnetic field. This aspect of the corona is remarkable also because of the long streamers stretching out like two great wings from the equatorial parts of the disk.

As a spectacle, the corona must be ranked among the finest sights in the heavens. In its meager contribution to astronomical knowledge it has thus far proved disappointing. It is true that the corona is displayed to us very infrequently and at these times only for a few minutes. But excellent photographs of many total solar eclipses during the past forty years are available for prolonged study. Such studies have so far yielded small return on the investment of time, energy, and money which have been spent on eclipse expeditions, often to remote parts of the world. Whether the corona has an important message to impart remains to be discovered.

PART IV

THE PLANETS AND THEIR SATELLITES

I

ORBITS AND ASPECTS OF THE PLANETS

THE orbits in which the planets revolve around their central luminary are in strictness ellipses, or slightly flattened circles. But the flattening is so slight that the eye would not notice it without measurement. The sun is not in the center of the ellipse but in a focus, which in some cases is displaced from the center by an amount that the eye can readily perceive. This displacement measures the eccentricity of the ellipse, which is much greater than the flattening. For example, in the case of Mercury, which moves in a very eccentric orbit, the flattening is only one fiftieth; that is, if we represent the greatest diameter of the orbit by fifty, the least diameter will be forty-nine. But the distance of the sun from the center of the orbit is ten on the same scale.

To show this we give a diagram of the orbits of the inner group of planets showing quite nearly their forms and respective locations. A simple glance will show that the orbits are much nearer together at some points than at others.

In explaining the various aspects and motions, real and apparent, of the planets, a number of technical expressions are used which we shall explain.

Inferior planets are those whose orbits lie within the

orbit of the earth. This class comprises only Mercury and Venus.

Superior planets are those whose orbits lie without that of the earth. These comprise Mars, the minor

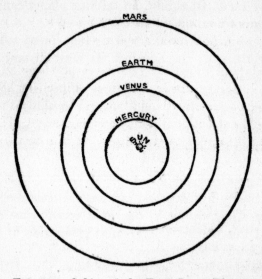

FIG. 23. *Orbits of the Four Inner Planets*

planets or asteroids, and all five of the outer group of major planets.

When a planet seems to us to pass by the sun, and so is seen as if alongside of it, it is said to be *in conjunction* with the sun.

An *inferior conjunction* is one in which the planet is between us and the sun.

A *superior conjunction* is one in which the planet is beyond the sun.

A little consideration will show that a superior

planet can never be in inferior conjunction, but an inferior planet has both kinds of conjunction.

A planet is said to be *in opposition* when it is in the opposite direction from the sun. It then rises at sunset, and *vice versa*. Of course, an inferior planet can never be in opposition.

The *perihelion* of an orbit is that point which is nearest the sun; the *aphelion* its most distant point from the sun.

As the inferior planets, Mercury and Venus, perform their revolutions, they seem to us to swing from one side of the sun to the other. Their apparent distance from the sun at any time is called their *elongation*.

The greatest elongation of Mercury is generally about twenty-five degrees, being sometimes more and sometimes less, owing to the great eccentricity of the orbit of this planet. The greatest elongation of Venus is almost forty-five degrees.

When the elongation of one of these planets is east from the sun we may see it in the west after sunset; when west we may see it in the east in the morning sky. As neither of them ever wanders from the sun farther than the distances we have stated, it follows that a planet seen in the east in the evening, or in the west in the morning, cannot be either Mercury or Venus.

No two orbits of the planets lie exactly in the same plane. That is, if we regard any one orbit as horizontal, all the others will be tipped by small amounts toward one side or the other. Astronomers find it convenient to take the plane of the earth's orbit, or the ecliptic plane, as the horizontal or standard one. As each orbit is centered on the sun it will have two opposite points which lie on the same horizontal plane as the earth's orbit. More exactly, these are the points at which the orbit intersects the plane of the ecliptic. They are called *nodes*.

The angle by which an orbit is tipped from the plane of the ecliptic is called its *inclination*. The orbit of Mercury has the greatest inclination, about 7°. The orbit of Venus is inclined 3° 24′; those of all the superior planets less, ranging from 0° 46′ in the case of Uranus to 2° 30′ in the case of Saturn, with the conspicuous exception of Pluto, whose orbit is inclined 17°.

DISTANCES OF THE PLANETS

Leaving out Neptune and perhaps Pluto, the distances of the planets follow very closely a rule known as Bode's Law, after the astronomer who first pointed it out. It is this: Take the numbers 0, 3, 6, 12, etc., doubling each as we go along. Then add 4 to each number, and we shall hit very nearly on the scale of distances of all the planets excepting Neptune, thus:

Mercury,	$0 + 4 =$	4;	actual distance	4
Venus,	$3 + 4 =$	7;	" "	7
Earth,	$6 + 4 =$	10;	" "	10
Mars,	$12 + 4 =$	16;	" "	15
Asteroids,	$24 + 4 =$	28;	" "	20 to 40
Jupiter,	$48 + 4 =$	52;	" "	52
Saturn,	$96 + 4 =$	100;	" "	95
Uranus,	$192 + 4 =$	196;	" "	192
Neptune,	$384 + 4 =$	388;	" "	301
Pluto,	$768 + 4 =$	772;	" "	396

On these actual distances we remark that astronomers do not use miles or other terrestrial measures to express distances between the heavenly bodies, for two reasons. In the first place, miles are too short; to use them would be like stating the distance between two cities in inches. In the next place, distances in the heavens cannot be fixed with the necessary exactness in our measures, whereas, if we take the sun's distance from the earth as the unit of measure, we can determine other distances between the planets with great precision in terms of this measure. So, to get the distances of the planets from the sun in astronomical measure, we have to divide the last numbers of the preceding table by ten, or insert a decimal point before the last figure of each.

We have not in this table distracted the attention of the reader by using unnecessary decimals. Actually, the distance of Mercury is 0.387, etc.; we have simply called it 0.4 and multiplied it by 10 to get the proportion for comparing with Bode's Law.

KEPLER'S LAWS

The motions of the planets in their orbits take place in accordance with certain laws laid down by Kepler, and therefore known as *Kepler's laws*. The first of these has already been mentioned; the orbits of the planets are ellipses, of which the sun is in one focus.

The second law is that the nearer the planet is to the sun the faster it moves. With more mathematical exactness, the areas swept over by the line joining the planet and sun in equal times are all equal.

The third law is that the cubes of the mean distances of the planets from the sun are proportional to the squares of their periods of revolution. This law requires some illustration. Suppose one planet to be four times as far from the sun as another. It will then be eight times as long going around it. This number is reached by taking the cube of four, which is sixty-four, and then extracting the square root, which is eight.

The unit of measure which the astronomer uses to express distances in the solar system being the mean distance of the earth from the sun, it follows that the mean distances of the inferior planets will be decimal fractions, as we have just shown, while those of the outer ones will vary from 1.5 in the case of Mars to 40 in the case of Pluto. If we take the cubes of all these distances and extract their square roots we shall have the periods of the revolution of the planets, expressed in years.

It will be seen that the outer planets are longer in getting around their orbits, not only because they have farther to go, but because they actually move more slowly. If, as in the case first supposed, the outer planet is four times as far from the sun, it will move only half as fast. This is why it takes eight times as long to get around. The speed of the earth in its orbit is 18.5 miles a second. But that of Neptune is only 3.5 miles a second, although it has thirty times as far to go. This is why it takes more than one hundred and sixty years to complete a revolution.

II

THE PLANET MERCURY

To SET forth what is known of the major planets we shall take them up in the order of their distance from the sun. The first planet reached will then be Mercury. It is not only the nearest planet to the sun, but much the smallest of the nine; so small, indeed, that, but for its situation, it would hardly be called a major planet. Its diameter is 50 per cent greater than that of the moon, but, the volumes of bodies being proportional to the cubes of their diameters, it has more than three times the volume of the moon.

With the exception of Pluto, Mercury has far the most eccentric orbit of all the major planets, though, in this respect, it is exceeded also by some of the minor planets to be hereafter described. In consequence, its distance from the sun varies between wide limits. At perihelion it is less than twenty-nine millions of miles from the sun; at aphelion it goes out to a distance of more than forty-three millions of miles. It performs its revolution around the sun in a little less than three months, to speak more exactly, in eighty-eight days. It therefore makes more than four revolutions in a year.

Performing more than four revolutions around the sun while the earth is performing one, Mercury comes to conjunction with the sun at certain regular though somewhat unequal intervals. To show the exact nature

of its apparent motion let the inner circle of the
diagram (Figure 24) represent the orbit of Mercury
and the outer one that of the earth. When the earth is
at E, and Mercury at M, the latter is in inferior conjunction with the sun. At the end of three months it

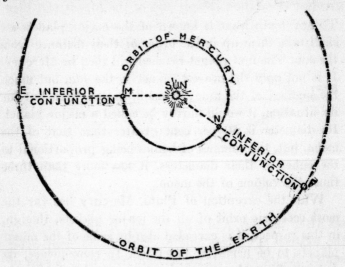

FIG. 24. *Conjunctions of Mercury with the Sun*

will have returned to the point M, but it will not yet
be in conjunction, because, in the meantime, the earth
has moved forward in its orbit. When the earth reaches
a certain point F, Mercury will have reached the point
N and will again be in inferior conjunction. This
revolution from one inferior conjunction to another is
called the *synodic* revolution of the planet. In the case
of Mercury this is somewhat less than one third more
than the time of actual revolution; that is to say, the
arc MN is a little less than one third of the circle.

Now suppose that when the earth is at E, Mercury, instead of being at M is near the highest point A of the orbit as represented in Figure 25. It will then be at its greatest apparent distance from the sun, as we see it from the earth, or, in technical language, at its greatest elongation. Being east of the sun, it will then

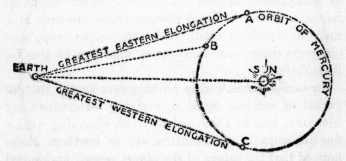

FIG. 25.   *Elongations of Mercury*

set after the sun, and may be seen in the twilight in the western sky from half an hour to an hour after sunset. At the opposite elongation, near C, it is west of the sun; then it rises before the sun and may be seen in the east in the morning twilight. As evening star, Mercury is best seen at eastern elongations which occur in the spring; as morning star at western elongations in the autumn.

THE APPEARANCE OF MERCURY

The best time to make a telescopic study of Mercury is late in the afternoon, when it is near east elongation, or shortly after sunrise, if it rises before the sun. Supposing it east of the sun, it will probably be visible in the telescope at any time after noon, but the air is generally disturbed by the sun's rays, so that it is hardly possible to make a good observation at that time. Late in the afternoon the air grows steadier, so that the planet can be better observed. But, after sunset, the planet is seen through a continually increasing extent of atmosphere, so that the blurring again begins to increase. Owing to these circumstances Mercury is a difficult planet to study in a satisfactory way, and observers differ very much as to what can be seen on its surface.

In earlier times, nearly all observers agreed that no period of rotation could be certainly determined for Mercury. But in 1889, Schiaparelli, observing with a fine telescope in the beautiful sky of northern Italy, noticed that the aspect of the planet seemed unchanged day after day. He was thus led to the conclusion that it always presents the same face to the sun, as the moon presents the same face to the earth. This view was shared by Lowell, observing at Flagstaff, Arizona; and it is now held by the majority of astronomers.

Owing to the various positions of Mercury relative to the sun it presents phases like those of the moon. These depend upon the relation of the dark and the illuminated hemispheres relative to the direction in which we see the planet. The hemisphere which is turned away from the sun, being in darkness, is always invisible to us. At superior conjunction the illuminated hemisphere is turned toward us, and the disk of the planet is round, like the full moon. As it moves from east elongation to inferior conjunction, more and more of the dark hemisphere is turned toward us, and less and less of the illuminated one. But this disadvantage is counterbalanced by the fact that the planet continually comes nearer during the interval, so that we get a better view of whatever portion of the illuminated hemisphere may be visible to us. Its apparent form and size at different times during its synodic revolution go through a series of changes similar to those shown in the next chapter in the case of Venus.

It is probable that Mercury has no atmosphere. It seems quite certain that, if it has one, it is too rare to reflect the light of the sun.

TRANSITS OF MERCURY

It will be readily seen that, if an inferior planet revolved around the sun in the same plane as the earth, we should see it pass over the sun's disk at every inferior conjunction. But no two planets revolve in the same plane. Of all the major planets, Pluto excepted, the orbit of Mercury has the largest inclination to that of the earth. In consequence, when in inferior conjunction, it commonly passes a greater or less distance to the north or to the south of the sun. If, however, it chances to be near one of its nodes at the time of conjunction, we shall see it with the telescope as a black spot passing across the sun's disk. This phenomenon is called a transit of Mercury. Such transits occur at intervals ranging between three and thirteen years. They are observed with much interest by astronomers because it is possible to determine with great precision the time at which the planet enters upon the solar disk, and leaves it again. Knowing these times, valuable information is afforded respecting the exact law of motion of the planet.

The first observation of a transit of Mercury was made by Gassendi on November 7, 1631. His observation is not, however, of any scientific value at the present time, owing to the imperfection of his instruments. A somewhat better but not good observation was made by Halley, in 1677, during a visit to the island of St. Helena. Since that time the transits have been observed with a fair degree of regularity. The following table shows the transits that will be visible during the next few years, with the regions of the earth in which each may be seen:

1937, May 11, Mercury will graze the south limb of the sun. The phenomenon will be visible in Europe, but will occur before the sun rises in America.

1940, November 10, visible in the Western and Pacific States.

1953, November 14, visible throughout the United States.

Observations of transits of Mercury since 1677 have brought out an interesting fact. The orbit of this planet is found to be slowly changing its position, its perihelion moving forward by about forty-three seconds a century farther than it ought to move in consequence of the attraction of all the known planets. This deviation was discovered, in 1845, by Leverrier, celebrated as having computed the position of Neptune before it had ever been recognized in the telescope. He attributed the discrepancy to the attraction of a planet, or group of planets, between Mercury and the sun. His announcement set people to looking for the supposed planet. About 1860, Lescarbault, a country physician of France, who possessed a small telescope, thought he had seen this planet passing over the disk of the sun. Another more experienced astronomer, however, who was looking at the sun on the same day, failed to see anything except an ordinary spot. It was probably this which misled the physician-astronomer. Now, for many years, the sun has been carefully scrutinized and photographed from day to day at several stations without anything of the sort being seen.

Still, it seemed possible that little planets so minute as to escape detection in passing over the sun's disk might revolve in the region in question. If so, their light would be completely obscured by that of the sky, so that they would not ordinarily be visible. But there was still a chance that, during a total eclipse of the sun, when the light is cut off from the sky, they could be seen. Observers have, from time to time, looked for them during total eclipses, and the powerful agency of photography has been invoked as well. A decisive answer was obtained at the total eclipse of 1901, when some fifty stars were photographed in the sun's vicinity, some as faint as the eighth magnitude, but they were all found to be known objects. It therefore seems certain that there can be no intramercurial planet much brighter than the eighth magnitude. It would take hundreds of thousands of such planets as this to produce the observed motion of Mercury. So great a number of these bodies would cause a far brighter illumination of the sky than any that we see. The result therefore seems to be conclusive against the view that the motion of the perihelion of Mercury can be produced by intramercurial planets. In addition to all these difficulties in supposing the planet to exist we have the difficulty that, if it did exist, it would produce a similar though smaller change in the position of the nodes of either Mercury or Venus, or both.

The general theory of relativity, formulated by Einstein, in 1915, requires the advance of Mercury's perihelion at the rate of 43″ a century faster than that calculated by Newton's theory of gravitation, and in practical agreement with the observed excess. It is one of several instances in which celestial phenomena seem to be more successfully represented by the relativity theory than by the older one.

III

OF ALL the star-like objects in the heavens the planet Venus is the most brilliant. The sun and moon are the only heavenly bodies outshining it. In a clear and moonless evening it may be seen to cast a shadow. If an observer knows exactly where to look for it and has a well-focused eye, it can be seen in the daytime when near the meridian, provided that the sun is not in its immediate neighborhood. When it is east of the sun it may be seen in the west, faintly before sunset and growing continually brighter as the sunlight diminishes. When west of the sun it rises in the morning before the sun, and may then be seen in the east. Under these circumstances it has been called the evening and morning star respectively. The ancients called it Hesperus when an evening star, and Phosphorus when a morning star. It is said that, in the early history of our race, Hesperus and Phosphorus were not known to be the same body.

If Venus is examined with the telescope, even one of low power, it will be seen to exhibit phases like those of the moon. This fact was ascertained by Galileo when he first directed his telescope toward the planet, and it afforded him strong evidence of the truth of the Copernican system. In accordance with a custom of the time he published this discovery in the form of an anagram—a collection of letters which, when subsequently put together, would state the discovery. Translated into English the anagram read, "The mother of the loves emulates the phases of Cynthia."

What we have said of the synodic motion of Mercury applies in principle to Venus and need not therefore be repeated. In Figure 26 the apparent size of

Fig. 26.   *Phases of Venus in Different Points of
Its Orbit*

the planet is shown in various parts of its synodic orbit. As the planet passes from superior to inferior conjunction its disk continually grows larger in apparent size, though we cannot see its entire outline. But the fraction of the disk illuminated continually becomes smaller, first having the shape of a half moon, and then the shape of a crescent, which grows thinner and thinner up to the time of inferior conjunction. In the latter position the dark hemisphere is turned toward us and the planet is invisible. Venus is at its greatest brightness about halfway between inferior conjunction and greatest elongation. It then sets about two hours after the sun, if east of it, and rises about two hours before the sun, if west of it.

ROTATION OF VENUS

The question of the rotation of Venus has interested astronomers and the public ever since the time of Galileo. But the difficulty of learning anything certain on the subject is very great, owing to the peculiar glare of the planet. When seen through a telescope no sharp and well-defined markings are visible. Instead of this there is a glare on the surface, varying by gentle gradations from one region to another, as if we were looking upon a globe of polished but slightly tarnished metal. Nevertheless, various observers have supposed that they could distinguish bright or dark spots. As far back as 1667, Cassini concluded from these seeming spots that the planet revolved on its axis in a little less than twenty-four hours. During the next century, Blanchini, an Italian observer, published an extensive treatise on the subject, illustrated with many drawings of the planet. His conclusion was that Venus requires more than twenty-four days to rotate on its axis. Schiaparelli, in 1890, arrived at a still different conclusion, namely, that Venus rotates on its axis in the same period that it revolves around the sun; in other words, both Mercury and Venus always present the same face to the sun, as the moon presents the same face to the earth. Schiaparelli reached this conclusion by noticing that a number of exceedingly faint spots could be seen on the southern hemisphere of Venus for several days in succession in the same position day after day. He could observe the planet through several hours on each day, and the constancy of the spots precluded the idea that the planet made one rotation and a little more in the course of a day. Lowell was led to the same conclusion by careful study of the planet at his Arizona observatory.

That careful observers of the markings on the disk of Venus have disagreed so widely as to the period of its rotation can be interpreted in only one way. The markings are very faint indeed. It is the present opinion that this planet rotates at a considerably slower rate than the earth does. Special observations with the spectroscope, and the absence of appreciable flattening at the poles of the planet, give evidence in this direction. But a period as long as 225 days is not entirely acceptable. Recent photographs by Ross, which show markings more clearly than the eye can discern them, suggest more rapid changes in the markings than would be likely to occur if the planet turned the same hemisphere always toward the sun. Ross assigns tentatively a rotation period of thirty days.

ATMOSPHERE OF VENUS

It is now well established that Venus is surrounded by an atmosphere which is probably denser than that of the earth. This was shown in a remarkable and interesting way during the transit of Venus over the sun's disk in 1882, which was observed by the writer at the Cape of Good Hope. When the planet was a little more than halfway on the disk, its outer edge appeared illuminated, as shown in Figure 27. This illumination, however, did not commence at the middle point of the arc, as it should have done had it been caused by regular refraction, but commenced at a point quite near one end of the arc. This appearance was explained by Russell, of Princeton, who showed that the atmosphere is so full of vapor that we cannot see the light of the sun by direct refraction through it. What we see is an illuminated stratum of clouds or vapor floating in an atmosphere. Such being the case, it is not at all

PART OF THE SUN.

FIG. 27. *Effect of the Atmosphere of Venus during the Transit of 1882*

likely that astronomers on the earth can ever see the solid body of the planet through these clouds. Hence the supposed spots could only have been temporary clouds, continually changing.

To illustrate the illusions to which the sight of even good observers may be subject, we may mention the fact that several such observers have supposed the whole hemisphere of Venus to be visible when the planet was near inferior conjunction. It then had the appearance familiarly known as "the new moon in the old moon's arms," with which everyone who observes our satellite when a narrow crescent is familiar. In the case of the moon it is well known that we thus see the dark hemisphere by the light reflected from the earth. But in the case of Venus there is no possibility of a sufficient reflection of light from the earth, or any other body. The appearance has sometimes been explained by a possible phosphorescence covering the whole hemisphere of Venus. But it is more likely due to an optical illusion. It has generally been seen in the daytime, when the sky is brightly illuminated, and when any faint light like that of phosphorescence would be completely invisible. To whatever we might attribute the light, it ought to be seen far better after the end of twilight in the evening than during the daytime. The fact that it is not seen then seems to be conclusive against its reality.

The appearance illustrates a well-known psychological law, that the imagination is apt to put in what it is accustomed to see, even when the object is not there. We are so accustomed to the appearance on the moon that when we look at Venus the similarity of the general phenomena leads us to make this supposed familiar addition to it.

The chance of photographing the surface of a planet successfully through its atmosphere is improved by the use of plates which are made specially sensitive to red or infra-red light, and by exposing them behind red filters. In this way clear views of the earth's surface have been secured from airplanes at high elevations when the photographer could not see the ground at all. Excellent photographs of the Andes several hundred miles away were recently made by the same procedure by Stevens from an airplane. He had to guess at the pointing of the camera, because he could not see the mountains through the haze.

Near the time of the favorable elongation of Venus in 1927, Ross photographed Venus in red and infra-red light with the great telescopes of the Mount Wilson Observatory. The disk of the planet appeared perfectly blank in the pictures. But with ultra-violet light his photographs showed conspicuous markings—the first to be clearly visible on this planet. They are cloud markings in the atmosphere which turns back most of the ultra-violet light of the sun before it can penetrate to the surface of the planet.

Bright spots at opposite extremities of the photographed disk of Venus bear some resemblance to the white polar caps of Mars, though they are less permanent. Dark bands across the disk suggest the cloud belts of Jupiter, and, like them, change form rapidly. Whether there are continents and oceans, vegetable and animal life, and perhaps intelligent life beneath the atmosphere of Venus, we can, at least for the present, only imagine.

TRANSITS OF VENUS

The transits of Venus across the sun's disk are among the rare phenomena of astronomy, as they occur, on the average, only once in sixty years. For many centuries past and to come there will be a regular cycle, bringing about four transits in two hundred and forty-three years. The intervals between the transits are one hundred and five and a half years, eight years, one hundred and twenty-one and a half years, eight years; then one hundred and five and a half years again, and so on. The dates of the last six transits and the two next to come are as follows:

1631, December 7,	1874, December 9,
1639, December 4,	1882, December 6,
1761, June 5,	2004, June 8,
1769, June 3,	2012, June 6.

Few persons now living are likely to see this phenomenon, as the next transit does not occur until 2004. Yet, the time when Venus will appear upon the disk on June 8 of that year can now be predicted for any point on the earth's surface, within a minute or two.

The interest which has attached to these transits during the past century arose from the fact that they were supposed to afford the best method of determining the distance of the sun from the earth. This fact and the rarity of the phenomenon led to the last four transits being observed on a large scale. In 1761, and again in 1769, the leading maritime nations sent observers to various parts of the world to note the exact time at which the planet entered upon and left the sun's disk. In 1874 and 1882, expeditions were fitted up on a large scale by the United States, Great Britain, France, and Germany. On the first of these occasions American parties occupied stations in China, Japan, and eastern Siberia on the north, and in Australia, New Zealand, Chatham Island, and Kerguelen Island in the south. In 1882, it was not necessary to send out so many expeditions, because the transit was visible in this country. In the southern hemisphere stations were occupied at the Cape of Good Hope and other points. The observations made by these expeditions proved of great value in determining the future motions of Venus, but it was found that other methods of determining the distance of the sun would lead to a more certain result.

IV

THE PLANET MARS

MUCH interest has in recent years been concentrated on the planet Mars. Its resemblance to our earth, its canals, climate, snowfall, and other remarkable features have all tended to interest us in its possible inhabitants. At the risk of disappointing those readers who would like to see certain proof that our neighboring world is peopled with rational beings, I shall endeavor to set forth what is actually known on the subject.

We begin with some particulars which will be useful in recognizing the planet. Its period of revolution is six hundred and eighty-seven days, or forty-three days less than two years. If the period were exactly two years, Mars would make one revolution while the earth made two, and we should see the planet in opposition at regular intervals of two years. But, as it moves a little faster than this, the earth requires from one to two months to catch up with it, so that the oppositions occur at intervals of two years and one or two months. This excess of one or two months makes up a whole year after eight oppositions; consequently, at intervals of fifteen or seventeen years, Mars will be in opposition at the same time of the year, and near the same point of its orbit. In this period the earth will have made fifteen or seventeen revolutions and Mars eight or nine.

The difference of a month or so in the interval between oppositions is due to the great eccentricity of the orbit, which is larger than that of any other major planet except Mercury and Pluto. Its value is 0.093, or nearly one tenth. Hence, when in perihelion, it is nearly one tenth nearer the sun than its mean distance, and when in aphelion nearly one tenth farther. Its distance from the earth at opposition will be different by the same amount, measured in miles, and hence in a much larger proportion to the distance itself. If opposition occurs when the planet is near perihelion, the distance from earth may be as small as thirty-five million miles; but if near the aphelion, more than sixty million miles. The result is that, at a favorable opposition, which can occur only in August or September, the planet will appear more than three times as bright as at an unfavorable opposition, occurring in February or March. Favorable oppositions occurred, for example, in 1877, 1892, 1909, and 1924; and the next one is scheduled for 1939.

Mars, when near opposition, is easily recognized by its brilliancy, and by the reddish color of its light, which is very different from that of most of the bright stars. It is curious that a telescopic view of the planet does not give so strong an impression of red light as does the naked eye view.

THE SURFACE AND ROTATION OF MARS

Huygens, about 1659, was the first one to recognize the variegated character of the surface of Mars as it appears in the telescope, and to make a drawing of the appearance which it presented. The features which he delineated can be recognized and identified to this day. By watching them it is easy to see that the planet rotates on its axis in a little more than one of our days (24h. 37m.).

This period of rotation is more accurately determined than the rotation period of any other planet except the earth. For two hundred years Mars has rotated at exactly this rate, and there is no reason to suppose that the period will change appreciably. The close approach to one of our days, the excess being only thirty-seven minutes, leads to the result that, on successive nights, Mars will, at the same hour, present nearly the same face to the earth. But, owing to the excess, it will always be a little farther behind on any one night than on the night before, so that, at the end of forty days, we shall have seen every part of the planet that is presented to the earth.

All that was known of the surface of Mars up to a quite recent period could be embodied in a map of the planet, showing the bright and dark regions, and in the fact that a white cap would be generally seen to surround each of its poles. When a pole was inclined toward us, and therefore toward the sun, this cap gradually grew smaller, enlarging again when the pole was turned from the sun. In the latter case it would be invisible from the earth, so that the growth could be recognized only by its larger size when it again came into sight. These caps were naturally supposed to be snow and ice which formed around the poles during the Martian winter and partly or wholly melted away during the summer.

THE CANALS OF MARS

In 1877, Schiaparelli discovered the so-called canals. They consist of streaks passing from point to point on the planet, and slightly darker than the general surface. Seldom has more misapprehension been caused by a mistranslation than in the present case. Schiaparelli called these streaks *canale*, an Italian word meaning channels. He called them so because it was then supposed that the darker regions of the surface were oceans, and the streams connecting the oceans were therefore supposed to be water, and so were called channels. But the translation "canals" led to a widespread notion that these streaks were the works of inhabitants, as canals on the earth are the works of men.

There has been some disagreement between astronomical authorities on the subject of these channels. This arises from the fact that they are not well-defined features on an otherwise uniform surface. Everywhere on the planet are found variations of shade—light and dark patches, so faint and ill defined that it is generally difficult to assign exact form and outline to them, running into each other by insensible gradations. The extreme difficulty of making them out at all, and the variety of aspects they present under different illuminations and in different states of our atmosphere, has resulted in a great variety of delineations of these objects. Drawings made by the observers at the Lowell Observatory show the channels as fine dark lines, so numerous as to form a network covering the greater part of the surface of the planet. In Schiaparelli's map they are rather broad faint bands, not nearly so well defined, nor so numerous, as in Lowell's drawings. An interesting feature of the latter is that the points where the channels cross each other are marked by dark round spots like circular lakes.

One of the best marked features of Mars is a large, dark, nearly circular spot, surrounded by white, which is called *Solis Lacus*, or the Lake of the Sun. All observers agree on this. They also agree in a considerable part as to certain faint streaks or channels extending from this lake. But when we go farther we find that they do not agree completely as to the number of these channels, nor is there an exact agreement as to the surrounding features. Another conspicuous marking is the *Syrtis Major*, the triangular dark spot first sketched by Huygens.

There is no longer any doubt as to the existence of the canals of Mars. They have been observed by many astronomers, and have been photographed successfully. In all probability they are somewhat broader, and less regular and artificial in appearance, than they seemed to some of the earlier observers. We accept the canals as natural features of the Martian landscape.

The surface of Mars shows, therefore, markings of great variety and interest. Of all the planets, except the earth, its surface can be studied with the telescope to the best advantage. It presents a reddish background which suggests barren, desert conditions. Against this background we see large blue-green spots; these were originally called "seas," and their special watery names have survived, as with the lunar seas, though neither are now regarded as bodies of water. Joining the seas, and sometimes passing through them,

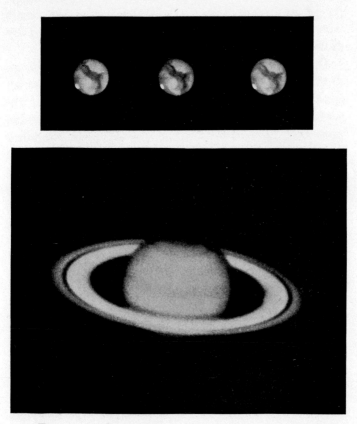

FIG. 28.—(above) *Mars showing Polar Cap.*
(below) *Saturn and its Rings.* (*From
photographs at Yerkes Observatory.*)

we observe the rather narrow dark streaks, the canals, whose original names have survived along with those of the seas.

The features which we have hitherto described do not belong to the two polar regions of the planet. Even when the snowcaps have melted away, these regions are seen so obliquely that it would be difficult to trace any well-defined features upon them. The interesting question is whether the caps which cover them are really snow which falls during the Martian winter and melts again when the sun once more shines on the polar regions. To throw light on this question we have to consider some recent results as to the atmosphere of the planet.

THE MARTIAN SEASONS

All recent observers are agreed that the atmosphere of Mars is much rarer than our own, and contains less aqueous vapor. This conclusion is reached from observations with both the telescope and the spectroscope. The most careful observations of the planet show that the features are rarely obscured by clouds in the Martian atmosphere.

Now snow can fall only through the condensation of aqueous vapor in the atmosphere. It does not therefore seem likely that much snow can fall on the polar regions of Mars.

Another consideration is that the power of the sun's rays to melt snow is necessarily limited by the amount of heat that they convey. In the polar regions of Mars the rays fall obliquely, and even if all the heat conveyed by them were absorbed, only a few feet of snow could be melted in the course of the summer. By far the larger proportion of the sunlight must be reflected from the white snow, which is also kept cool by the intense radiation into perfectly cold space. We therefore conclude that the amount of snow that can fall and melt around the polar regions of Mars must be very small, being probably measured by inches at the outside.

As the thinnest fall of snow would suffice to produce a white surface, this does not prove that the caps are not snow. But it seems more likely that the appearance is produced by the simple condensation of aqueous vapor upon the intensely cold surface, producing an appearance similar to that of hoarfrost, which is only frozen dew. This seems to me the most plausible explanation of the polar caps. It has also been suggested that the caps may be due to the condensation of carbonic acid. We can only say of this, that the theory, while not impossible, seems to lack probability.

There appears to be life on the planet Mars. A few years ago this statement was commonly regarded as fantastic. Now it is commonly accepted. We refer, however, to forms resembling our vegetable life and not to intelligent human life, for there is no evidence to prove the existence of such life on Mars. The planet possesses air and water, although in very small quantities compared with the earth, to be sure; and in the tropics the surface is above freezing at noon, although far below freezing most of the time even there and of course all the time on the rest of the planet.

The view that Mars shows seasonal changes, first expressed a few decades ago, is now concurred in by

many astronomers. The Martian equator is inclined
23½° to its orbit. Its poles, like those of the earth, are
turned alternately toward and away from the sun.
Thus the planet has seasons resembling ours, although
its different seasons are about twice as long as ours
because its year is almost twice as long.

As the spring season advances in one of the Martian
hemispheres, the white polar cap shrinks, and the dark
markings in that hemisphere become more conspicuous
and greener. As the summer season progresses and the
polar cap entirely or almost disappears, the dark
markings fade noticeably and turn brown. The most
plausible interpretation of these seasonal changes
which has yet been suggested is that they are the
effects of vegetation which flourishes in the Martian
spring season and dies down with the approach of
autumn.

Recent photographs of Mars, particularly at the
Lowell and Lick observatories, through filters of
various colors, emphasize details of its surface and
atmosphere. Photographed in ultra-violet light, the
surface markings—the large green spots and some of
the canals—show very clearly. We recall that with the
same procedure photographs of Venus reveal nothing
but a blank disk, and we conclude that the Martian
atmosphere must be the more transparent. The ultra-
violet photographs of Mars, on the other hand, show,
as we should expect, very little surface detail. They
are pictures of its atmosphere, and they sometimes
reveal clouds, or at least something resembling the
clouds on the earth.

The really surprising feature is that the white polar

caps are indistinct in the infra-red photographs and conspicuous in those taken in ultra-violet light. Wright's conclusion is that the white caps we see are not snow caps at all, but fog banks over the polar regions, although there may be smaller caps of snow beneath them.

THE SATELLITES OF MARS

The two satellites of Mars were discovered by Hall, at the Naval Observatory, in 1877. They had failed of previous detection owing to their extreme minuteness. It was not considered likely that a satellite could be so small as these were found to be, and so no one had taken the trouble to make a careful search with any great telescope. But, when once discovered, they were found to be by no means difficult objects. Of course, the ease with which they can be seen depends on the position of Mars both in its orbit and with respect to the earth. They are never visible except when the planet is near its opposition. At each opposition they may be observed for a period of three, four, or even six months, according to circumstances. At an opposition near perihelion they may be seen with a telescope less than twelve inches in diameter; how small a one will show them depends on the skill of the observer, and the pains he takes to cut off the light of the planet from his eye. Generally a telescope ranging from twelve to eighteen inches in diameter is necessary. The difficulty in seeing them arises entirely from the glare of the planet. Could this be eliminated, they could doubtless be seen with much smaller instruments.

Owing to the glare, the outer one is much easier to see than the inner one, although the inner one is the brighter of the two.

Hall assigned the name *Deimos* to the outer and *Phobos* to the inner, these being the attendants of Mars in ancient mythology. Phobos has the remarkable peculiarity that it revolves around the planet in 7 hours 39 minutes, the shortest period of any yet known in the solar system. This is less than one third the time of the planet's rotation on its axis. Consequently, to the inhabitants of the planet, its nearest moon rises in the west and sets in the east.

Deimos performs its revolution in 30 hours 18 minutes. The result of this rapid motion is that some two days must elapse between its rising and setting.

Phobos is only 3,700 miles from the surface of the planet. It must therefore be an interesting object to the inhabitants of Mars, if they have telescopes.

In size these bodies are the smallest visible to us in the solar system, with the possible exception of some of the fainter asteroids. Photometric estimates give the diameter of Deimos as five miles, and that of Phobos as ten miles. Their sizes as we view them are therefore not very different from that of an apple hanging over Boston and seen from New York.

The satellites have been most useful to the astronomer in enabling him to learn the exact mass of Mars, which proves to be only one ninth the earth's mass. How this is done will be explained in a subsequent chapter, where the methods of weighing the planets are set forth.

V

THE GROUP OF MINOR PLANETS

THE seeming gap in the solar system between the orbits of Mars and Jupiter naturally attracted the attention of astronomers as soon as the distances of the planets had been accurately laid down. It became very striking when Bode announced his law. There was a row of eight numbers in regular progression, and every number but one represented the distance of a planet. That one place was vacant. Was the vacancy real, or was it only because the planet which filled it was so small that it had escaped notice?

This question was settled by Piazzi, an Italian astronomer who had a little observatory in Palermo in Sicily. He was an ardent observer of the heavens and was engaged in making a catalogue of stars whose positions could be determined with his instrument. On January 1, 1801, he inaugurated the new century by finding a star where none had existed before; and this star soon proved to be the long-looked-for planet. It received the name of *Ceres*, the goddess of the wheat field.

It was a matter of surprise that the planet should be so small; and when its orbit became known it proved to be very eccentric. But new revelations were soon to come. Before the new planet had completed a revolution after its discovery, Olbers, a physician of Bremen, who employed his leisure in astronomical observations and researches, found another planet revolving in the same region. Instead of one large planet there were two small ones. He suggested that these might be fragments of a shattered planet, and that, if so, more would probably be found. The latter part of the conjecture proved true. Within the next three years two more of these little bodies were discovered, making four in all.

Thus the matter remained for some forty years. Then, in 1845, Hencke, a German observer, found a fifth planet. The year following a sixth was added, and then commenced the steady series of discoveries which, proceeding year by year, have carried the number past the thousand mark.

HUNTING ASTEROIDS

Up to 1890 these bodies had been found by a few observers who devoted especial attention to the search and caught the tiny stars as the hunter does game. They would lay traps, so to speak, by mapping the many stars in some small region of the sky near the ecliptic, familiarize themselves with their arrangement, and then watch for an intruder. Whenever one appeared, it was found to be one of the group of minor planets, and the hunter put it into his bag.

About 1890 the photographic art was found to offer a much easier and more effective means of finding these objects. The astronomer would point his telescope at the sky, start the driving clock, and photograph the stars with a rather long exposure, perhaps half an hour, more or less. The stars proper would be taken on the negative as small round dots. But if a planet happened to be among them it would be in motion, and thus its picture would be taken as a short line and not as a dot. Instead of scanning the heavens the observer had only to scan his photographic plate, a much easier task, because the planet could be recognized at once by its trail. In this way, Max Wolf at Heidelberg has discovered more than five hundred asteroids.

Most of the recently discovered asteroids are very faint; yet the number seems to increase with their faintness. It is estimated that as many as one hundred thousand are within the reach of present telescopes. Even the larger of these bodies are so small that they appear only as star-like points in ordinary telescopes, and their disks are hard to make out even with the most powerful instruments. Ceres, the largest asteroid, is 480 miles in diameter. About a dozen exceed a hundred miles. The size of the smallest can be inferred only in a rough way from their brightness. They may be twenty or thirty miles in diameter.

ORBITS OF THE ASTEROIDS

The orbits of some of these bodies are very eccentric. In the case of Hidalgo, the eccentricity is 0.65, which means that at perihelion it is two thirds nearer the sun than its mean distance, and at aphelion two thirds more distant. At the greatest distance from the sun, this asteroid is as remote as the planet Saturn.

The large inclination of some of the orbits is also noteworthy. In several cases it exceeds 20°; in that of Hidalgo it is 43°.

The idea that these bodies might be fragments of a planet which had been shattered by some explosion is now abandoned. The orbits range through too wide a space ever to have joined, as they would have done if the asteroids had once formed a single body. In the philosophy of our time these bodies have been as we see them since the beginning. On the theory of the nebular hypothesis the matter of all the planets once formed rings of nebulous substance moving round the sun. In the case of all the other planets the material of these rings gradually gathered around the densest point of the ring, thus agglomerating into a single body. But it might be that the ring forming the minor planets did not collect in this way, but separated into innumerable fragments.

According to the planetesimal hypothesis of Chamberlin and Moulton, the asteroids resulted from collisions of fewer small pieces than the larger planets. Some of them, therefore, did not acquire the nearly circular and only slightly inclined orbits which many collisions would be likely to produce.

GROUPING OF THE ORBITS

There is a feature of the orbits of these bodies which may throw some light on the question of their origin. I have explained that the planetary orbits are nearly circles, but that these circles are not centered on the sun. Now imagine that we are looking down upon the solar system from an immense height, and suppose that the orbits of the minor planets are visible as finely drawn circles. These circles would appear to interlace

and cross each other like an intricate network, filling a
broad ring of which the outer diameter would be nearly
or quite double the inner one.

But suppose we could pick all these circles up, as if
they were made of wire, and center them all on the sun,
without changing their size. The diameters of the larger
ones would be double those of the smaller, so that the
circles would fill a broad space, as shown in Figure 29.

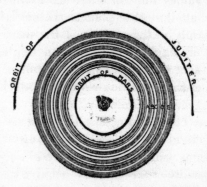

FIG. 29.   *Separation of the Minor Planets into
Groups*

Now, the curious fact is that they would not fill the
whole space uniformly, but would be collected into distinct groups. These groups are shown in Figure 29,
and, on a different plan, and more completely, in Figure 30, which is arranged on a plan explained as follows: Every planet performs its revolution in a certain
number of days, which is greater the farther the planet
is from the sun. Since the complete circumference of
the orbit measures 1,296,000″, it follows that if we divide this number by the period of revolution, the quo-

tient will show through what angle, on the average, the
planet moves along its orbit in one day. This angle is
called the *mean motion* of the planet. In the case of the
minor planets it ranges from 400″ to
more than 1,000″, being greater the
shorter the period of revolution and the
nearer the planet is to the sun.

Now we draw a vertical line and mark
off on it values of the mean motion,
from four hundred to one thousand seconds, differing by ten seconds. Between
each pair of marks we make as many
points as there are planets having mean
motions between the limits. For example, between 550″ and 560″ there are
three dots. This means that there are
three planets in the list selected having
mean motions between 550″ and 560″.
There are also four planets between
560″ and 570″, and one between 570″
and 580″. Then there are no more till
we pass 610″, when we find six planets
between 610″ and 620″, followed by a
multitude of others.

Fig. 30. *Dis-*

Examining the diagram we are able *tribution of the*
to distinguish five or six groups. The *Orbits of the*
outermost one is between 400″ and 460″, *Minor Planets*
and is nearest to Jupiter. The times of revolution are
not far from eight years. Then there is a wide gap
extending to 560″, when we have a group of ten
planets between 540″ and 580″. From this point down-
wards the planets are more numerous, but we find very

sparse or empty points at 700″, 750″, and 900″. Now the most singular feature of the case is that these empty spaces are those in which the motion of a planet would have a simple relation to that of Jupiter. A planet with a mean motion of 900″ would make its circuit round the sun in one third the time that Jupiter does; one of 600″ in half the time; one of 750″ in two fifths of the time. It is a law of celestial mechanics that the orbits of planets having these simple relations to another undergo great changes in the course of time from their action on each other. It was therefore supposed by Kirkwood, who first pointed out these gaps in the series, that they arose because a planet within them could not keep its orbit permanently. But it is curious that there are no gaps, but, on the contrary, groups of planets where the mean motions are respectively two thirds of and equal to that of Jupiter.

THE ASTEROID EROS

One of these bodies is so exceptional as to attract our special attention. All the hundreds of minor planets known up to 1898 moved between the orbits of Mars and Jupiter. But in the summer of that year Witt, of Berlin, found a planet which, at perihelion, came far within the orbit of Mars—in fact, within fourteen million miles of the orbit of the earth. He named it *Eros*. The eccentricity of its orbit is so great that at aphelion the planet is considerably outside the orbit of Mars. Moreover, the two orbits, that of the planet and of Mars, pass through each other like two links of a chain, so that if the orbits were represented of wire they would hang together.

Owing to the inclination of its orbit, this planet wanders far outside the limits of the zodiac. When near the earth, in 1900, it was for a time so far north that it never set in our middle latitudes, and passed the meridian north of the zenith. This peculiarity of its motion was doubtless one reason why it was not found sooner. During its near approach in the winter of 1900–'01, Eros was closely scrutinized and found to vary in brightness from hour to hour. Careful observation has shown that these changes occur in a regular period of five and a quarter hours. It has been supposed by some that this asteriod is really made up of two bodies revolving round each other—perhaps actually joined into one. But it seems more likely that the variations of light are caused by the presence of light and dark regions on the surface of the little planet, which therefore change in brightness according as bright or dark regions predominate on the surface of the hemisphere turned toward us. The case is made perplexing by the gradual disappearance of the variations, at times.

Variations of light which might be due to a rotation on their axes have been suspected in the case of other asteroids besides Eros, but nothing has yet been settled.

From a scientific point of view Eros is most interesting because, coming so near the earth from time to time, its distance may be measured with great precision, and the distance of the sun, as well as the dimensions of the whole solar system, thus fixed with greater exactness than by any other method. Unfortunately, the nearest approaches occur only at very long intervals.

In 1900 Eros approached the earth within about thirty millions of miles. On January 30, 1931, its distance was only sixteen million miles, which is closer than any other planet ever comes to the earth, although this one may approach us still nearer, by more than two million miles. The next close approach of Eros will occur in 1975.

VI

JUPITER AND ITS SATELLITES

JUPITER, the "giant planet," is, next the sun, the largest body of the solar system. It is, in fact, more than three times as large and about three times as massive as all the other planets put together. Yet, such is the preponderating mass of our central luminary that the mass of Jupiter is less than one thousandth part that of the sun.

Near the time of opposition which occurs about a month later from year to year, this planet may easily be recognized in the evening sky, by both its brightness and its color. It is, then, next to Venus and occasionally Mars, the brightest star-like object in the heavens. It can easily be distinguished from Mars by its whiter color. If we look at it with a telescope of the smallest size, even with a good ordinary spyglass, we shall readily see that instead of being a bright point, like a star, it is a globe of very appreciable dimensions. We shall also see what look like two shadowy belts crossing the disk. These were noticed and pictured two hundred years ago by Huygens. As greater telescopic power was used, it was found that these seeming belts resolved themselves into very variegated cloud-like forms, and that they vary, not only from month to month, but even from night to night. By careful observation of the appearance which they present from hour to hour, and from night to night, it was found that the planet rotates on its axis in about 9 hours 55 minutes. The astronomer may therefore in the course of a single ing see every part of the surface of the planet presented his view in succession.

Two features presented by the planet will at once strike the observer with the telescope. One of these is that the disk does not seem uniformly bright; it gradually shades off near the limb which, instead of being bright and hard, is somewhat soft and diffuse. In this respect the appearance forms quite a contrast to that presented by the moon or Mars. The shading off toward the edge is attributed to a dense atmosphere surrounding the planet.

The other feature to which we allude is the ellipticity of the disk. Instead of being perfectly round, the planet is flattened at the poles, like our earth, but in a much greater degree. The most careful observer, viewing the earth from another planet, would see no deviation from the spherical form. The conspicuous flattening of Jupiter is owing to its rapid rotation on its axis, which causes its equatorial regions to bulge out.

VISIBLE SURFACE OF JUPITER

The features of Jupiter, as we see them with a telescope, are almost as varied as those of the clouds which we see in our atmosphere. There are commonly elongated strata of clouds, apparently due to the same cause that produces stratified clouds in our atmosphere, namely, currents of air. Among these clouds, round white spots are frequently seen. The clouds are sometimes of a rosy tinge, especially those near the equator. ... re darkest and most strongly marked in middle ...udes, both north and south of the equatorial regions. It is this that produces the appearance of dark belts in a small telescope.

The appearance of Jupiter is, in almost every point, very different from that of Mars, the most strongly marked difference consisting in the entire absence of permanent features. Maps of Mars may be constructed and their correctness tested by observations generation after generation, but no such thing as a permanent map of Jupiter is possible.

Notwithstanding this lack of permanence, features have been known to endure through a number of years. The most remarkable of these was the great red spot, which appeared in middle latitudes, on the southern hemisphere of the planet, about the year 1878. For several years it was a very distinct object about 30,000 miles long, readily distinguished by its color. After ten years it began to fade away, but not at a uniform rate. Sometimes it would seem to disappear entirely, then would brighten up once more. These changes continued but, since 1892, faintness or invisibility has been the rule. If the spot finally disappeared, it was in so uncertain a way that no exact date for the last observation of it can be given. Some observers report it to be visible from time to time. A larger white spot underlying it, first noticed a century ago, is still plainly visible.

CONSTITUTION OF JUPITER

The question of the constitution of this planet is still an unsettled one. There is no one hypothesis that readily explains all the facts.

Perhaps the most remarkable feature of the planet is its small density. Jupiter's diameter is about eleven times that of the earth. It follows that, in volume, it must exceed the earth more than thirteen hundred times. But its mass is only a little more than three hundred times that of the earth. It follows from this that its density is much less than that of the earth; as a matter of fact, it is only about one third greater than the density of water. A simple computation shows that the force of gravity at its surface is between two and three times that at the surface of the earth. Under this gravitation we might suppose its interior to be enormously compressed and its density to be great in comparison. Such would certainly be the case were it made up of solid or fluid matter of the same kind that composes the surface of the earth. From this fact alone the conclusion would be that its outer portions at least are composed of aëriform matter. But how reconcile this form with the endurance of the red spot through so many years? This is the real difficulty.

Nevertheless, the hypothesis is one which we are forced to accept without great modification. Besides the evidence of an encompassing atmosphere, as shown by the constantly changing aspect of the planet, we have another almost conclusive piece of evidence in the law of rotation. It is found that Jupiter resembles the sun in that its equatorial region rotates in less time than the regions north of middle latitude, although the circuit they have to make is longer. This is probably a law of rotation of gaseous bodies in general. The difference in the time of rotation at the equator and in middle latitudes is about five minutes. That is to say, the equatorial region rotates in nine hours fifty minutes and those in middle latitudes in nine hours fifty-five minutes. This corresponds to a difference of velocity of the motion between the two amounting to about two hundred miles an hour; a seemingly impossible difference were the surface liquid.

The idea that the planet can emit much light of its own seems to be negatived by the fact that the satellites completely disappear when they pass into its shadow. We may therefore say with entire certainty that Jupiter does not give enough light to enable us to see a satellite by that light alone. We can hardly suppose that this would be the case if the satellite received one per cent as much light from the planet as it does from the sun. It is also found that the light which Jupiter sends out is somewhat less than that which it receives from the sun. That is to say, all the light which it gives out, when estimated in quantity, may be reflected light, without supposing the planet brighter than white bodies on the surface of the earth. Recent radiometric measurements give no indication of internal heat.

The hypothesis which best lends itself to all the facts seems to be that the planet has a solid, cold nucleus, whose density may be comparable with that of the earth or any other solid planet, and that the small average density of the entire mass is due to the extensive atmosphere which surrounds this nucleus.

THE SATELLITES OF JUPITER

When Galileo first turned his little telescope on the planet Jupiter he was delighted and surprised to find it accompanied by four minute companions. Watching them from night to night, he found them to be in revolution around their central body as, upon the theory not fully accepted in his time, the planets revolve around the sun. This remarkable resemblance to the solar system was a strong point in favor of the Copernican theory.

These bodies can be seen with a common spyglass, or even a good opera glass. It has even been supposed that good eyes sometimes see them without optical assistance. They are certainly as bright as the smallest stars visible to the naked eye, yet the glare of the planet would seem to be an insuperable obstacle to their visibility, even to the keenest vision.

Although they have received the names Io, Europa, Ganymede, and Callisto, these four bright satellites of Jupiter are known more often by numbers in order of their distances from the planet. The second satellite is slightly smaller than our moon, and the first is a little larger. The third and fourth satellites, 3,200 miles in diameter, are 50 per cent larger than the moon; they are the largest satellites in the solar system, greater even than the planet Mercury. But because their distance from the sun is five times the moon's distance, all four combined shine upon Jupiter with a brightness less than a third that of full moonlight on the earth. Just as the moon turns one face always toward the earth, each of these satellites turns the same hemisphere toward Jupiter. In other words, they rotate and revolve in the same periods of time.

Only four satellites were known until 1892; then Barnard, at the Lick Observatory, discovered a fifth, much nearer the planet and much fainter than the four others. It makes a revolution in a little less than twelve hours, the shortest period of revolution known except that of the inner satellite of Mars. Yet it is a little longer than the rotation period of the planet. The next outer one, or the innermost of the four previously known, still called the first satellite, revolves in about one day eighteen and a half hours, while the outermost of the four bright satellites requires nearly seventeen days to perform its circuit.

The sixth and seventh satellites of Jupiter were discovered by Perrine at the Lick Observatory, in 1904 and 1905. At nearly the same mean distance of more than seven million miles from the planet, their periods of revolution are between eight and nine *months*. Still another and more distant pair were discovered a little later, increasing the number to nine. The eighth satellite was discovered in 1908, by Melotte at the Greenwich Observatory, the ninth in 1914, by Nicholson at the Lick Observatory. Their distances from the planet vary from fifteen to twenty million miles, and their periods of revolution exceed two *years*. In addition to being the most distant from their primary of all satellites in the solar system, they are unlike the great majority of the members of our system in that they revolve from east to west.

All four outer satellites have more eccentric orbits than the inner ones. They are very small, having diameters of a hundred miles, or even considerably less, so that they are visible only with large telescopes. It is suggested that their origin was different from that of the inner satellites. Some astronomers have supposed that they may be captured asteroids.

During their course around the planet the four bright satellites present many interesting phenomena, which can be observed with a moderate sized telescope. These are their *eclipses* and *transits*. Of course, Jupiter, like any other opaque body, casts a shadow. As the satellites make their round they nearly always pass through the shadow during that part of their course which is beyond the planet. Exceptions sometimes occur in the case of the fourth and most distant satellite, which may pass above or below the shadow, as our moon passes above or below the shadow of the earth. When a satellite enters the shadow, it fades away gradually, and finally disappears from sight altogether.

For the same reason the satellites generally pass across the disk of the planet in that part of their course which lies on this side of it. The general rule is that, when a satellite has impinged on the planet, it looks brighter than the latter, owing to the darkness of the planet's limb. But, as it approaches the central regions, it may look darker than the background of the planet. Of course, this does not arise from any change in the brightness of the satellite, but only from the fact, already mentioned, that the planet is brighter in its central regions than at its limb.

Equally interesting is the shadow of a satellite which, under such circumstances, may often be seen upon the planet, looking like a black dot crossing alongside the satellite itself.

The phenomena of Jupiter's satellites, including their transits and those of their shadows, are all predicted in the nautical almanacs, so that an observer can always know when to look for an eclipse or transit.

The eclipses of the inner of the four older satellites occur at intervals of less than two days. By noting their times, an observer in unknown regions of the earth can determine his longitude. He has first to determine the error of his watch on local time by certain simple astronomical observations, quite familiar to astronomers and navigators. He then observes the local time at which an eclipse of the satellite takes place. He compares this with the predicted Greenwich time which can be found from the data in the almanac. The difference gives his longitude according to the system set forth in our chapter on Time and Longitude.

But this method is not very accurate. Observations of the time of such an eclipse are doubtful to a large fraction of a minute, or of fifteen miles at the equator.

VII

AMONG the planets, Saturn is next to Jupiter in size
and mass. It performs its revolution round the sun in
twenty-nine and a half years. When the planet is visible
the casual observer will generally be able to recognize
it without difficulty by its slightly reddish tint, and by
the steadiness of its light when the neighboring stars
are twinkling.

Although Saturn is far from being as bright as Jupiter, its rings make it the most magnificent object in the
solar system. There is nothing else like them in the
heavens, and it is not surprising that they were an
enigma to the early observers with the telescope. To
Galileo they first appeared as two handles to the planet.
After a year or two they disappeared from his view. We
now know that this occurred because, owing to the motion of the planet in its orbit, they were seen edge-on,
and are then invisible in a telescope, because they are
so thin. But the disappearance was a source of great
embarrassment to the Tuscan philosopher, who is said
to have feared that he had been the victim of some
illusion, and he therefore ceased to observe Saturn.
He was then growing old, and left to others the task of
continuing his observations. Soon the handles reappeared, but there was no way of learning what they

were. After more than forty years the riddle was solved by Huygens, the great Dutch astronomer and physicist, who announced that the planet is surrounded by a thin plane ring, nowhere touching it, and inclined to the ecliptic.

SATELLITES OF SATURN

Besides the rings, Saturn is surrounded by a retinue of nine satellites, sharing with Jupiter the distinction of having the greatest number. The existence of a tenth has been suspected, but awaits confirmation. They are very unequal in size and distance from the planet. One, Titan, may be seen with a small telescope; the faintest are visible only in very powerful ones.

Titan was discovered by Huygens just as he had made out the true nature of the rings. And hereby hangs a little tale which has come out through the publication of Huygens's correspondence. Following a practice of the time, the astronomer sought to secure priority for his discovery without making it known, by concealing it in an anagram, a collection of letters which, when properly arranged, would inform the reader that the companion of Saturn makes its revolution in fifteen days. A copy of this was sent to Wallis, the celebrated English mathematician. In his reply the latter thanked Huygens for his attention and said he also had something to say, and gave a collection of letters longer than that of Huygens. When the latter interpreted his anagram to Wallis, he was surprised to receive in reply a solution of the Wallis anagram announcing the very same discovery, but, of course, in different language and at greater length. It turned out that Wallis, who was expert in ciphers, wanted to demonstrate the futility of the system and had managed to arrange his own letters so as to express the discovery, after he knew what it was.

VARYING ASPECTS OF SATURN'S RINGS

The Paris Observatory was founded in 1666 as one of the great scientific institutions of France which adorned the reign of Louis XIV. Here Cassini discovered the division in the ring, showing that it is really composed of two rings, one outside the other, and in the same plane. The outer of these rings has somewhat the appearance of being again divided, by a line called the Encke division, after the astronomer who first noticed it, but the exact nature of this division is still in doubt. It certainly is not sharp and well defined like the Cassini division, but only a slight shade.

To make clear the varying appearance of the rings we give a figure showing how they and the planet would look if we could see them perpendicularly (which we never can). We notice first, in Figure 31, the dark Cassini division, separating the rings into two, an inner and an outer one, the latter being the narrower. Then, on the outer ring, we see the faint Encke division, which is much less marked and much harder to see than the other. Passing to the inner ring, we notice that the latter shades off gradually on the inner edge, where there is a gray border called the "crape ring." This was first described by Bond, of the Harvard Observatory, and was long supposed to be a separate and distinct ring. But careful observation shows that such is not the case. The crape ring joins onto the ring outside of it, and the latter merely fades away into the other.

The rings of Saturn are inclined about twenty-seven

FIG. 31. *Perpendicular View of the Rings of Saturn*

degrees to the plane of its orbit, and they keep the same direction in space as the planet revolves round the sun. The effect of this will be seen in Figure 32, which shows the orbit of the planet round the sun in perspective. When the planet is at A the sun shines on the north (upper) side of the ring. Seven years later, when the planet is at B, the ring is presented to the sun edgewise. After the planet passes B, the sun shines on the south (lower) side at an inclination which continually increases till the planet reaches C, when the inclination is at its greatest, twenty-seven degrees. Then the tilt of the rings with respect to the sun's direction, diminishes as the planet passes to **D**, at which point the edge of the ring is again presented to the sun. From this point to **A** and **B** the sun again shines on the north side.

The earth is so near the sun in comparison with Saturn that the rings appear to us nearly as they would

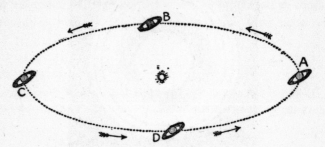

Fig. 32. *Showing how the Direction of the Plane of Saturn's Rings Remains Unchanged as the Planet Moves round the Sun*

to an observer on the sun. There is a period of fifteen years, during which we see the north side of the rings, and at the middle of which we see them at the widest angle. As the years advance, the angle grows narrower, and the rings are seen more and more edgewise till they close up into a mere line crossing the planet, or perhaps disappear entirely. Then they open out again, to close up in another fifteen years. A disappearance occurred in 1921 and another will take place in 1936.

With this view of what the shape of the rings really

is, we may understand their appearance to us. The rings are always seen very obliquely, never at a greater angle than twenty-seven degrees. The general outline presented by the planet and rings is that seen in Figure 33. The best views are obtained when the rings are at a considerable angle. The divisions and the crape ring are then seen to best advantage. The shadow of the globe of the planet on the ring appears as a dark notch. A dark line crossing the planet like a border to the inner ring is the shadow of the ring on the planet.

NATURE OF THE RINGS

When it became accepted that the laws of mechanics, as we learn them on the earth, govern the motions of the

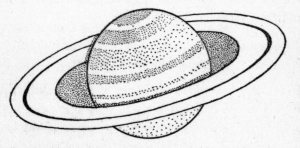

Fig. 33. *The Rings of Saturn, Inclined*

heavenly bodies, another riddle was presented by the rings of Saturn. What keeps the rings in place? What keeps the planet from running against the inner ring and producing, to modify Addison's verse, a "wreck of matter and crash of worlds" that would lay the whole beautiful structure in ruins? Before observational evidence became available, it was understood that the rings cannot be continuous surfaces, as they seem to be. They could not hold together under the great tidal force exerted by Saturn. Instead, they are composed of many small bodies, revolving like little satellites around the planet. This view had to be accepted, but was long without observational proof, until it was brought out by Keeler with the spectroscope. He found that when the light of the rings is spread out into a spectrum, the dark spectral lines are displaced in such a way as to show that different parts of the rings are revolving round the planet at unequal angular speeds. At the outer edge the revolution is slowest; the speed continually increases toward the inner edge, and is everywhere the same that a satellite would have if it revolved round the planet at that distance.

SATELLITES OF SATURN

In making known his discovery of the satellite Titan, Huygens congratulated himself that the solar system was now complete. There were now seven great bodies and seven small ones, the magic number of each. But within the next thirty years Cassini exploded all this mysticism by discovering four more satellites of Saturn. Then, after the lapse of a century, the great Herschel found yet two more. Finally, the eighth was found by Bond at the Harvard Observatory, in 1848, and the ninth by W. H. Pickering, in 1898.

The following is a list of the nine satellites, with

their distances from the planet, in miles, their periods
of revolution, and their discoverers:

No.	Name.	Discoverer.	Date of Discovery.	Distance from Planet.	Period. of Revolution.
					d. h.
1	Mimas....	Herschel....	1789	115,000	0 23
2	Enceledus.	Herschel....	1789	148,000	1 9
3	Tethys....	Cassini.....	1684	183,000	1 21
4	Dione.....	Cassini.....	1684	234,000	2 18
5	Rhea......	Cassini.....	1672	327,000	4 12
6	Titan.....	Huygens....	1655	759,000	15 23
7	Hyperion..	Bond.......	1848	920,000	21 7
8	Iapetus...	Cassini.....	1671	2,210,000	79 8
9	Phoebe....	Pickering...	1898	8,034,000	550

The most noteworthy features of this list are the wide
range of distances among the satellites, and the relation
between the periods of revolution of the four inner ones.
The five inner ones seem to form a group by themselves.
Then there is a gap exceeding in breadth the distance
of the innermost of the five, when we have another
group of two, Titan and Hyperion. Then there is a gap
wider than the distance of Hyperion, outside of which
comes Iapetus, and finally Phoebe, nearly four times
more remote.

An interesting relation among the periods is that the
period of the third satellite is almost exactly twice that
of the first; and that of the fourth almost twice that of
the second. Also, four periods of Titan are almost exactly equal to three of Hyperion.

The result of the relation last mentioned is a certain

very curious action of these two satellites on each other, through their mutual gravitation. To show this we give a diagram of the orbits. That of Hyperion, the outer of the two, is very eccentric, as will be seen by the

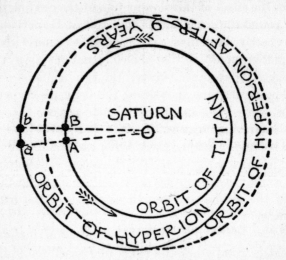

FIG. 34. *Orbits of Titan and Hyperion, showing their relation*

figure. Suppose the satellites to be in conjunction at a certain moment; Titan, the inner and larger of the two at a point A, Hyperion at the point *a* just outside. At the end of sixty-five days Titan will have made three revolutions and Hyperion four, which will bring them again into conjunction at very nearly, but not exactly, the same point. Titan will have reached the point B, and Hyperion *b*. At a third conjunction the two will be a little above the line B*b*, and so on. Really the conjunctions occur closer together than we have been able to draw them in Figure 34. In the course of nineteen years the point of conjunction will have slowly moved all round the circle, and the satellites will again be in conjunction at A.

Now the effect of this slow motion of the conjunction-point round the circle is that the orbit of Hyperion, or, more exactly, its longer axis, is carried round with the conjunction-point, so that the conjunctions always occur where the distance between the two orbits is greatest. The dotted line shows how the orbit of Hyperion is thus carried halfway round in nine years.

An interesting feature of this action is that it is, so far as we know, unique, there being no case like it elsewhere in the solar system. But there may be something quite similar in the mutual action of the first and third, and of the second and fourth satellites of Saturn on each other.

A yet more striking effect of the mutual attraction of the matter composing the rings and satellites is that, excepting the two outer satellites, these bodies all keep exactly in the same plane. The effect of the sun's attraction, if there were nothing to counteract it, would be that in a few thousand years the orbits of these bodies would be drawn around into different plances, all having, however, the same inclination to the plane of the orbit of Saturn. But, by their mutual attraction, the planes of the orbits are all kept together as if they were solidly attached to the planet. It is noteworthy also that the outmost satellite revolves around the planet from east to west, like the two outer satellites of Jupiter.

PHYSICAL CONSTITUTION OF SATURN

There is a remarkable resemblance between the physical make-up of this planet and that of its neighbor Jupiter. They are alike remarkable for their small density, Saturn being even less dense than water. Another point of likeness is the rapid rotation; Saturn turns on its axis in 10 hours 14 minutes, a little more than the rotation period of Jupiter. The surface of the planet also seems to be variegated with cloud-like forms, similar to those of Jupiter, but fainter, so that they cannot be seen with equal distinctness.

What has been said of the probable cause of the small density of Jupiter applies equally to Saturn. The probability is that the planet has a comparatively small but massive nucleus, surrounded by an immense atmosphere, and that what we see is only the outer surface of the atmosphere.

VIII

URANUS AND ITS SATELLITES

URANUS is the seventh of the major planets in the order
of distance from the sun. It is commonly considered a
telescopic planet; but one having good eyesight can
easily see Uranus without artificial help, if he only
knows exactly where to look for it, so as to distinguish
it from the numerous small stars having the same appearance.

Uranus was discovered in 1781 by William Herschel, who at first supposed it to be the nucleus of a
comet. But its motion soon showed that this could not
be the case, and before long the discoverer found that it
was a new addition to the solar system. In gratitude to
his royal benefactor, George III, he proposed to call
the planet *Georgian Sidus*, a name which was continued
in England for some seventy years. Some continental
astronomers proposed that it should be called after its
discoverer, and the name *Herschel* was often assigned
to it. But by 1850, the name *Uranus*, originally proposed by Bode, became universal.

When the orbit of the planet was determined, so that
its course in former years could be mapped out, the
fact was brought to light that it had been seen and
recorded nearly a century before, as well as a few years
previously. Flamsteed, Astronomer Royal of England,
while engaged in cataloguing the stars, had marked it

down as a star on five occasions between 1690 and 1715. What was yet more singular, Lemonnier, at the Paris Observatory, had recorded it eight times in the course of two months, December, 1768, and January, 1769. But he had never reduced and compared his observations, and not till Herschel announced the planet did Lemonnier know how great a prize had lain for ten years within his grasp.

The period of revolution of Uranus is eighty-four years, so that its position in the sky changes but slowly from year to year.

The distance of Uranus is about twice that of Saturn. In astronomical units it is 19.2; in our familiar measures 1,782,000,000 miles.

Owing to this great distance, it is hard to see with certainty any features on its surface. In a good telescope the planet appears as a pale disk with a greenish hue. Some observers have fancied that they saw faintly marked features on its surface. Observations with the spectroscope show that Uranus rotates on its axis once in 10.8 hours, in the same direction as that in which the satellites revolve.

THE SATELLITES OF URANUS

There are four of these bodies moving round Uranus. The two outer ones can be seen in a telescope of twelve inches aperture or more; the inner ones only in the most powerful telescopes. They are named Ariel, Umbriel, Titania, and Oberon, in order of their distances from the planet, which range from 119,000 to 364,000 miles.

The history of these bodies is somewhat peculiar. Besides the two brighter ones, Herschel, before 1800, thought he caught glimpses from time to time of four others, and thus it happened that for more than half a century Uranus was credited with six satellites. This was because during all that time no telescope was made which could claim superiority over Herschel's.

Then about 1845, Lassell, of England, undertook the making of reflecting telescopes, and produced his two great instruments, one of two, the other of four feet aperture. The latter he afterwards took to the Island of Malta, in order to make observations under the fine sky of the Mediterranean. Here he and his assistant entered upon a careful examination of Uranus, and reached the conclusion that none of the additional satellites supposed by Herschel had any existence. But, on the other hand, two new ones were found so near the planet that they could not have been seen by any previous observer. During the next twenty years these newly found bodies were looked for in vain with the best telescopes then in use in Europe, and some astronomers professed to doubt their existence. But in the winter of 1873 they were found with the twenty-six-inch telescope of the Naval Observatory, in Washington, which had just been completed, and were shown to move in exact accordance with the observations of Lassell.

The most remarkable feature of these bodies is that their orbits are nearly perpendicular to the orbit of the planet. The result is that there are two opposite points of the latter orbit where that of the satellite is seen edgewise. When Uranus is near either of these points, we, from the earth, see the satellites moving as if swinging up and down in a north and south direction on each side of the planet, like the bob of a pendulum. Then, as the planet moves on, the apparent orbits slowly open out. At the end of twenty years we see them perpendicularly. They then seem to us almost circular, but appear to close up again year after year as the planet moves on its course. The orbits were last seen edgewise in 1924, and will be again so seen about 1945.

IX

NEPTUNE AND ITS SATELLITE

NEPTUNE comes next in order of distance from the sun. In size and mass it is not very different from Uranus, but its greater distance, 30 astronomical units, instead of 19.2, makes it fainter and harder to see. It is far below the limit of visibility to the naked eye, but a moderate-sized telescope shows it, if one can distinguish it from the numerous stars of similar brightness that stud the heavens.

The disk of Neptune is to be made out only with a telescope of considerable power. It is then seen to be of a bluish or leaden tint, perceptibly different from the seagreen of Uranus. Since no markings can be discerned on the disk of this planet, nothing can be known by direct observation about its rotation on its axis. Observations with the spectroscope show that the period of rotation is 15.8 hours.

The discovery of Neptune, in 1846, is regarded as one of the most remarkable triumphs of mathematical astronomy. Its existence was made known by its attraction on the planet Uranus before any other evidence had been brought out. The history of the circumstances leading to the discovery is so interesting that we shall briefly mention its main points.

HISTORY OF THE DISCOVERY OF NEPTUNE

During the first twenty years of the nineteenth century, Bauvard, of Paris, an eminent mathematical astronomer, prepared new tables of the motions of Jupiter, Saturn, and Uranus, then supposed to be the three outermost planets. He took the deviations of these planets, produced by their attraction on each other, from the calculations of Laplace. He succeeded fairly well in fitting his tables to the observed motions of Jupiter and Saturn, but found that all his efforts to make tables that would agree with the observed positions of Uranus were fruitless. If he considered only the observations made since the discovery by Herschel, he could get along; but no agreement could be obtained with those made previously by Flamsteed and Lemonnier, when the planet was supposed to be a fixed star. So he rejected these old observations, fitted his orbit into the modern ones, and published his tables. But it was soon found that the planet began to move away from its calculated position, and astronomers began to wonder what was the matter. It was true that the deviation, measured by a naked eye standard, was very small; in fact, if there had been two planets, one in the real and one in the calculated position, the naked eye could not have distinguished them from a single star. But the telescope would have shown them well separated.

Thus the case stood until 1845. At that time it occurred to Leverrier, in Paris, that the deviations were probably caused by the attraction of an unknown planet outside of Uranus. He proceeded to calculate in what orbit a planet should move to produce them, and laid his result before the Academy of Sciences in the summer of 1846.

It happened that, before Leverrier commenced his work, an English student at the University of Cambridge, John C. Adams, had the same idea and set about the same work. He got the result even before Leverrier did, and communicated it to the Astronomer Royal. Both computers calculated the present position of the unknown planet, so that, were it possible to distinguish it from a fixed star, it would only have been necessary to search in the region indicated in order to find the planet. Unfortunately, however, Airy was incredulous as to the matter, and did not think the chance of finding the planet sufficient to go through the laborious operation of a search until his attention was attracted by the prediction of Leverrier, and the close agreement between the two computers was remarked.

The problem of finding the planet was now taken up. Very thorough observations were made upon the stars in the region by Challis at the Cambridge Observatory. I must explain that, as it was not easy with the imperfect instruments of that time to distinguish so small a planet from the great number of fixed stars which studded the heavens around it, it was necessary to proceed by determining the position of as many stars as possible several times, in order that, by a comparison of the observations, it could be determined whether any of them had moved out of its place.

While Challis was engaged in this work, Leverrier wrote to Galle of the Berlin Observatory, giving him the predicted location of the planet among the stars.

Now it happened that the Berlin astronomers had just completed a map of that part of the sky in which the planet was located. So, on the very evening after the letter was received, they took the map to the telescope and proceeded to search about to see if any object was seen in the telescope which was not on the map. Such an object was very soon found, and, by comparing its position with that of the stars around it, it seemed to have a slight motion. But Galle was very cautious and waited for the discovery to be confirmed on the night following. Then it was found to have moved so much that no doubt could remain, and he wrote Leverrier that the planet actually existed.

When this news reached England, Challis proceeded to examine his own observations, and found that he had actually observed the planet on two occasions. Unfortunately, however, he had not reduced and compared his observations, and so failed to recognize the object until after it had been seen at Berlin. Astronomers have honored both Leverrier and Adams for the discovery of Neptune.

THE SATELLITE OF NEPTUNE

Of course the newly found planet was observed by astronomers the world over. Lassell soon found that Neptune is accompanied by a single satellite some three thousand miles in diameter.

Its distance from Neptune is 220,000 miles, almost the same as the moon's distance from the earth; but its period of revolution is only 5 days 21 hours, which shows that Neptune is seventeen times more massive than the earth.

The satellite revolves from east to west in a nearly circular orbit which is inclined 20° to Neptune's equator. In the course of nearly six hundred years, this orbit, keeping the same inclination, slides completely around toward the east. This regression is caused by the bulging of the planet's equator. Observations of the speed of the regression have permitted the calculation of the extent of the bulge of Neptune's equator; it is too small to be definitely detected in the tiny disk which this remote planet shows in the telescope.

Bulging at the equator suggests rotation. The extent of the bulge, together with knowledge of the planet's interior condition, gives evidence concerning the period of the rotation. But in this case the spectroscope has given an easier solution. From the slanting lines in Neptune's spectrum, Moore, at the Lick Observatory, in 1928, derived the period of the rotation as 15.8 hours. The direction of rotation is from west to east.

X

PLUTO

THE discovery of Neptune, which has just been described, did not close the problem of the apparent misbehavior of Uranus. Even after Neptune's attraction for Uranus had been taken into account, this planet did not keep faithfully to the new course assigned to it. It is true that the differences between calculated and observed positions were now much smaller—so small, in fact, as to make it questionable in the minds of many astronomers whether an unknown planet was to be held accountable for them. The problem of discovering a new planet, if indeed it existed, was made very difficult by the minuteness of the discrepancies in the motion of Uranus, and by the certainty that a new planet would be a faint object even with the telescope.

Percival Lowell, at his observatory in Arizona, was among those who worked on this problem. Lowell calculated the orbit of a possible trans-Neptunian planet. Then he and the other astronomers at the Lowell Observatory undertook to find it with the telescope. The search was photographic. Plates were taken of the region of the sky in which the new planet was supposed to be. A few days later, other plates were taken of the same region and compared with the earlier ones, to ascertain whether any star had changed its position. If so, it would not be a star at all, but a planet; and if fortune favored, it might be the planet sought.

Mr. Lowell died in 1916, but the search kept on. There were many disappointments, because there are many asteroids—tiny planets revolving mostly between the orbits of Mars and Jupiter—objects which resemble stars, being distinguished from stars by their motions. As the search continued, moving objects were found on the plates, many of them; but time after time they proved to be asteroids and not the more remote planet for which the astronomers were looking. In January, 1930, the photographs showed a moving object, and one moving slowly enough to be the planet beyond Neptune. It was near the star Delta in the constellation Gemini. Was it really the planet sought, or was it simply another asteroid whose normally swift motion was arrested temporarily? Time would tell. The object was watched eagerly night after night. It did not speed up. The search was over, and a new planet was discovered. The discovery was announced on March 13, 1930; C. O. Lampland being the discoverer.

Then followed a careful examination of old photographs of the skies for records of the new planet before its discovery. Several were found, going back as far as 1919. These valuable finds gave the information required for the calculation of the orbit of the planet. The period of revolution around the sun turned out to be 249 years, and the average distance from the sun 39.6 times the earth's distance.

On the average, the trans-Neptunian planet is 900 million miles beyond Neptune. But its orbit is so far from circular—more so in fact than any other principal planet—that it cuts inside the orbit of Neptune. Is there danger, then, of collision? None at all. The

orbit of the trans-Neptunian planet is inclined in such
a way that, although it is at times farther away than
Neptune and at other times nearer the sun, the least
possible distance of the two planets is 240 million
miles.

The name of the new planet is Pluto, which was considered appropriate in two respects. The first two let-

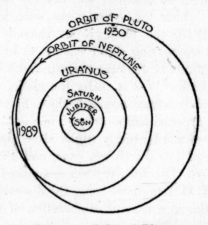

Fig. 35.   *Orbit of Pluto*

ters of the name, PL, are the initials of Percival Lowell, founder of the Lowell Observatory at Flagstaff,
Arizona, where the discovery was made. Also, Pluto
was said, by those who named the planet, to be the god
of the outer darkness. More authentically perhaps he
was god of the underworld; and it was not especially
dark down there. It might have been better, as an
astronomer suggested recently, if the name Amphitrite
had been adopted instead. Amphitrite was Neptune's
wife. Pluto could then have been reserved for another

planet still more remote, if there be one. But it is a small matter.

But what of the planet Pluto itself? In size and mass it resembles the earth more nearly than the giant planets which are its nearer neighbors. It appears as a yellow star visible only in large telescopes. The details of its surface and of its atmosphere are at present unknown. One thing is certain. The temperature must be very low there—too low for life to exist. From Pluto the sun would appear only as a point of light, and its brightness would be only three hundred times greater than full moonlight with us. Certainly it would not be a pleasant place to live.

But now comes a most interesting part of the story. No sooner did the study of photographs reveal the existence of a planet new to us, than astronomers began to calculate its orbit and its size. It proved to be very small, perhaps only one-tenth the size of the earth. Was it then possible that its existence could cause all the variations in the motion of Uranus, as Mr. Lowell had supposed? One could guess, but only careful calculations could give a definite answer. The largest amount of this work was carried out by our foremost living authority on the subject, Prof. Ernest W. Brown, of Yale University, and his studies give a definite answer. He found the effect of Pluto on Uranus to be slight; so slight that, as he says, Pluto "could not have been predicted by calculations of its effect on Uranus such as those made by Lowell."

Lowell's calculations remain only of academic interest. What he did accomplish was through the use of his private fortune in founding and endowing an ob-

servatory which took part in the now general study of
the heavens by photography, and searched these photographs with special reference to finding a possible new
planet. Long after his death this particular object
was attained. In consequence we know that one more
major planet exists, and so the whole solar system can
be better understood. Are there any other planets beyond Pluto? Perhaps so. Only the future can tell.

XI

DISTANCES in the heavens may be determined by a method similar to that employed by an engineer in determining the distance of an inaccessible object—say a mountain peak. Two points, A and B, are taken as a base line from which to measure the distance of a third point, C. Setting up his instrument at A, the engineer measures the angle between B and C. Setting it up at B he measures the angle between A and C. Since the sum of the three angles of a triangle is always one hundred and eighty degrees, the angle at C is found by subtracting the sum of the angles at A and B from that quantity. It will readily be seen that the angle at C is that subtended by the base line as it would appear if viewed by an observer at C. Such an angle is, in a general way, called a *parallax*. It is the difference of direction of the point C as seen from the points A and B.

It will readily be seen that, with a given base line, the greater the distance of the object the less will be its parallax. At a sufficiently great distance the latter will be so small that the observer cannot get any evidence of it. To all appearance the lines B C and A C will then have the same direction. The distance at which the parallax cannot be made out depends, of course, on the accuracy of the measurement and the length of the base line.

The moon being the nearest of all the heavenly bodies has the largest parallax. This angle is nearly one degree, taking as the base line the radius of the earth at the equator. The moon's distance can therefore be determined with the greatest precision by measurement. Even Ptolemy, who lived only one or two centuries after Christ, was able to make an approximate measure of the distance of the moon. But the

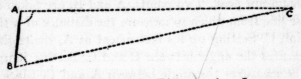

FIG. 36. *Measure of the Distance of an Inaccessible Object by Triangulation*

parallax of the sun or of a planet is so small that its determination requires more refined instruments.

The ends of the base line used in the determination may be any two points on the earth's surface—say the observatories of Greenwich and the Cape of Good Hope. In the case of the transits of Venus, which we have already described, there were a number of different stations at various points on the earth's surface, from which the direction of Venus at the beginning and end of its transit could be inferred. This method of determining distances is called *triangulation*.

The idea of a triangulation, as thus set forth, gives an understanding only of the general principle involved in the problem. The actual determination of the parallax requires a combination of observations too complex to be described in the present book, but the fundamental principle is that just explained.

In order to get the dimensions of the whole solar system, it is only necessary to know the distance of any one planet from us at any given moment. The planet Mars and the little asteroid Eros offer special advantages for determining the scale. The orbits and motions of all the planets are mapped down with the greatest possible exactness, but with the map before us we are in the position that one would be who had a very exact map of a country, only there was no scale of miles upon it. So he would be unable to measure the distance from one point to another on his map until he knew the scale. It is the scale of our map of the solar system which the astronomer stands in need of and which he has not, even with the most refined instruments, yet been able to determine as accurately as he could wish.

The fundamental unit aimed at is that already described—the mean distance of the earth from the sun. Measures of parallax are by no means the only method of determining this distance. Within the past century other methods have been developed, some of which are fully as accurate as the best measures of parallax, perhaps even more so.

MEASUREMENT BY THE MOTION OF LIGHT

One of the most simple and striking of these methods makes use of the velocity of light. By observations of the eclipses of Jupiter's satellites, made when the earth was at different points of its orbit, it has been found that light passes over a distance equal to that of the earth from the sun in about five hundred seconds. This determination has been made in another way by the aberration of the stars. This is a slight change in their directions due to the combined motion of the earth and the ray of light by which we see the star. It is found that light travels from the sun to the earth in 498.6 seconds. It follows that if we can find how far light will travel in one second, we can determine the distance of the sun by multiplying the result by 498.6. According to Michelson's recent measurement, the velocity of light is 186,284 miles in a second. Multiply this by 498.6 and we have nearly 92,900,000 miles for the distance of the sun from the earth.

MEASUREMENT BY THE SUN'S GRAVITATION

A third method of determining the scale of the solar system rests on the measures of the sun's gravitation upon the moon. One effect of this is that, as the moon performs its monthly revolution round the earth, it is at its first quarter a little more than two minutes behind its average position, to which it catches up at full moon, and passes; so that at last quarter it is two minutes ahead of the mean position. Toward new moon it falls behind again to the average place. Thus a slight swing goes on in unison with the moon's motion around the earth. The amount of this swing is inversely proportional to the distance of the sun. Hence, by measuring this amount, the distance may be determined.

The fourth method also rests on gravitation. If we only knew the exact relation between the mass of the earth and that of the sun; that is to say, if we could determine precisely how many times heavier the sun is than the earth, we could compute at what distance the earth must be placed from the sun in order to revolve around it in one year. The only difficulty, therefore, is to weigh the earth against the sun. This is most exactly done by finding the change in the position of the orbit of Venus produced by the earth's attraction. By comparing the positions of the orbit of Venus by its transits in 1761, 1769, 1874, and 1882, it is found that the orbit has a progressive motion, indicating that the mass of the sun is 332,600 times that of the earth and moon combined. Thus we are enabled to compute the distance of the sun by still another method.

RESULTS OF MEASUREMENTS OF THE SUN'S DISTANCE

These and other methods give for the sun's geocentric parallax, that is to say, the change in the direction of its center at sunrise or sunset as viewed from the center of the earth and a point on the equator, slightly more than 8″.80. This displacement is much too small to be detected with the unaided eye, but it is an angle large enough to be easily visible with the telescope. It follows that the earth viewed from the sun would appear as a point of light to the naked eye, and as a tiny disk with the telescope.

Knowing the sun's parallax and the radius of the earth at the equator, it is a simple matter to calculate the sun's mean distance. The best value of this distance is slightly less than 92,900,000 miles.

Expressed in miles, the sun's distance from the earth seems enormous. Of course, it is very great. Expressed in terms of the speed of light or of radio transmission, the distance is only a little more than eight minutes, while the distance of the nearest star exceeds four light-years. To an observer on the nearest star, the sun would appear as a star, and the earth could not be discerned with our greatest telescope; and if it could be discerned, only the largest telescopes could see the sun and earth separately. The distance between these two bodies, which seems so vast to us, would subtend an angle less than a second of arc.

The mean distance from the earth to the sun is known as the "astronomical unit." It provides the scale for our map of the solar system, by which we determine the distances of the other planets. Moreover, it is the great base line for the measurement of the distances of the stars and other celestial objects which lie beyond the solar system. On this account astronomers have tried by every possible means to measure this distance very accurately.

XII

GRAVITATION AND THE WEIGHING OF THE PLANETS

WE HAVE learned something of the orbits of the planets round the sun; but the following of the orbit is not the fundamental law of the planet's motion; the latter is determined by gravitation alone. The law of gravitation, as stated by Newton, is that every particle of matter in the universe attracts every other particle, with a force which varies inversely as the square of the distance between them. All the other processes of nature are in some way varied or modified by heat and cold, by time or place, by the presence or absence of other bodies. But no operation that man has ever been able to perform on matter changes its gravitation in the slightest. Two bodies gravitate by exactly the same amount, no matter what we do with them, no matter what obstacles we interpose between them, no matter how fast they move.

The motions of the planets are governed by their gravitation. Were there only a single planet moving round the sun it would be acted on by no force but the sun's attraction. By purely mathematical calculation it is shown that such a planet would describe an ellipse, having the sun in one focus. It would keep going round and round in this ellipse forever. But in accordance with the law, the planets must gravitate towards each other. This mutual gravitation is far less than that toward the sun, because in our solar system the planets are of much smaller mass than the central body. In consequence of this mutual attraction the planets deviate from the ellipse. Their orbits are very nearly, but not exactly, ellipses. Still, the problem of their motion is one of pure mathematical demonstration. It has occupied the ablest mathematicians of the world since the time of Newton. Every generation has studied and added to the work of the preceding one. One hundred years after Newton, Laplace and Lagrange derived more complete explanations of the changes in form and position of the elliptical orbits of the planets. These changes can be calculated thousands, tens of thousands, or even hundreds of thousands of years in advance. Thus it is known that the eccentricity of the earth's orbit round the sun is now slightly diminishing, and that it will continue to diminish for about forty thousand years. Then it will increase so that in the course of many thousands more of years it will be greater than it now is. The same is true of all the planets. Their orbits gradually change their form back and forth through tens of thousands of years, like "great clocks of eternity which count off ages as ours count off seconds." The reader would be justified in some incredulity as to the correctness of these predictions for thousands of years to come, were it not for the striking precision with which the motions of the planets are actually predicted for the present by the mathematical astronomer. This precision is reached by determining the effect of each planet on the motions of all the other planets. We might predict the motions of these bodies by assuming that each of them moves round the sun in a fixed ellipse, which, as I have just said, would be the case if it were not attracted by any other body. Our predictions would then, from time to time, be in error by amounts which might amount to large fractions of a degree; perhaps, in the course of a long time, to even more.

But, taking account of the attraction of all the other planets, the prediction is so exact that the refined observations of astronomy hardly show any appreciable deviation. The history of the discovery of Neptune, which was mentioned in the preceding chapter, affords the most striking example that we possess of the certainty of these predictions.

HOW THE PLANETS ARE WEIGHED

I shall now endeavor to give the reader some idea of the manner in which the mathematical astronomer reaches these results. He must, of course, know the pull each planet exerts upon the others. This is proportional to the *mass* of the attracting planet. This word is often taken to mean quantity of matter, and around us on the surface of the earth it has nearly the same meaning as the word weight. We may therefore say that, when the astronomer determines the mass of a planet, he is weighing it. He does this on the same principle by which the butcher weighs a ham in the spring balance. When the butcher picks the ham up he feels a pull of the ham toward the earth. When he hangs it on the hook, this pull is transferred from his hand to the spring of the balance. The stronger the pull the farther the spring is pulled down. What he reads on the scale is the strength of the pull. You know that this pull is simply the attraction of the earth on the ham. But, by a universal law of force, the ham attracts the earth exactly as much as the earth does the ham. So what the butcher really does is to find how much or how strongly the ham attracts the earth, and he calls that pull the weight of the ham. On the same principle, the astronomer finds the weight of a body by finding how strong is its attractive pull on some other body.

In applying this principle to the heavenly bodies, we meet at once a difficulty that looks insurmountable. We cannot get up to the heavenly bodies to do our weighing. How then shall we measure their pull? I must begin the answer to this question by explaining more exactly the difference between the *weight* of a body and its *mass*. The weight of objects is not the same all over the world; a thing which weighs thirty pounds in New York would weigh an ounce more than thirty pounds in a spring balance in Greenland, and nearly an ounce less at the equator. This is because the earth is not a perfect sphere, but a little flattened, and also because it is rotating. Thus weight varies with the place. If a ham weighing thirty pounds were taken up to the moon and weighed there, the pull would only be five pounds, because the moon is so much smaller and lighter than the earth. But there would be just as much ham on the moon as on the earth. There would be another weight on the planet Mars, and yet another on the sun, where it would weigh some eight hundred pounds. Hence, the astronomer does not speak of the weight of a planet, because that would depend on the place where it was weighed; but he speaks of the mass of the planet, which means how much planet there is, no matter where you might weigh it.

At the same time we might, without any inexactness, agree that the mass of a heavenly body should be fixed by the weight it would have at some place agreed upon, say New York. As we could not even imagine a planet at New York, because it may be larger than the earth itself, what we are to imagine is this: Suppose the planet could be divided into a great number of equal parts and one of these parts brought to New York and weighed. We could easily find its weight in pounds or tons. Then multiply this weight by the number of parts, and we shall have a weight of the planet. This would be what the astronomers might take as the mass of the planet.

With these explanations, let us see how the weight of the earth is found. The principle we apply is that round bodies of the same specific gravity attract small objects on their surface with a force proportional to the diameter of the attracting body. For example, a body two feet in diameter attracts twice as strongly as one of a foot, one of three feet three times as strongly, and so on. Now, our earth is about forty million feet in diameter; that is, ten million times four feet. It follows that if we made a little model of the earth four feet in diameter, having the average specific gravity of the earth, it would attract a particle with one ten-millionth part of the attraction of the earth. We have shown in our chapter on the earth how the attraction of such a model has actually been measured, with the result of showing that the total mass of the earth is five and one half times that of an equal bulk of water. Thus this mass becomes a known quantity.

We come now to the planets. I have said that the mass or weight of a heavenly body is determined by its attraction on some other body. There are two ways in which the attraction of a planet may be measured. One is by its attraction on neighboring planets, causing them to deviate from the orbits in which they would move if left to themselves. By measuring the deviations, we can determine the amount of the pull, and hence the mass of the planet.

The reader will readily understand that the mathematical processes necessary to get a result in this way must be very delicate and complicated. A much simpler method can be used in the case of those planets which have satellites revolving round them, because the attraction of the planet can be determined by the motions of the satellite. The first law of motion teaches us that a body in motion, if acted on by no force, will move in a straight line. Hence, if we see a body moving in a curve, we know that it is acted on by a force in the direction toward which the motion curves. A familiar example is that of a stone thrown from the hand. If the stone were not attracted by the earth it would go on forever in the line of throw, and leave the earth entirely. But under the attraction of the earth it is drawn down and down, as it travels onward, until finally it reaches the ground. The faster the stone is thrown, of course, the farther it will go, and the greater will be the sweep of the curve of its path. If it were a rifle bullet, the first part of the curve would be

nearly a right line. If we could fire a projectile hori-
zontally from the top of a high mountain with a velocity of five miles a second, and if it were not resisted
by the air, the curvature of the path would be equal
to that of the surface of our earth, and so the ball
would never reach the earth, but would revolve round
it like a little satellite in an orbit of its own. Could
this be done the astronomer would be able, knowing
the velocity of the ball, to calculate the attraction of
the earth. The moon is a satellite, moving like such a
ball, and an observer on Mars would be able, by measuring the orbit of the moon, to determine the attraction of the earth as well as we determine it by actually
observing the motion of falling bodies around us.

Thus it is that when a planet like Mars or Jupiter
has satellites revolving around it, astronomers on the
earth can observe the attraction of the planet on its
satellites and thus determine its mass. The rule for
doing this is very simple. The cube of the distance between the planet and satellite is divided by the square
of the period of revolution. The quotient is a number
which is proportional to the mass of the planet. The
rule applies to the motion of the moon round the earth
and of the planets round the sun. If we divide the cube
of the earth's distance from the sun, say ninety-three
millions of miles, by the square of three hundred and
sixty-five and a quarter, the days in a year, we shall
get a certain quotient. Let us call this number the sun-
quotient. Then, if we divide the cube of the moon's
distance from the earth by the square of its time of
revolution, we shall get another quotient, which we
may call the earth-quotient. The sun-quotient will

come out about three hundred and thirty thousand times as large as the earth-quotient. Hence it is concluded that the mass of the sun is three hundred and thirty thousand times that of the earth; that it would take this number of earths to make a body as heavy as the sun.

I give this calculation to illustrate the principle; it must not be supposed that the astronomer proceeds exactly in this way and has only this simple calculation to make. In the case of the moon and earth, the motion and distance of the former vary in consequence of the attraction of the sun, so that their actual distance apart is a changing quantity. So what the astronomer actually does is to find the attraction of the earth by observing the length of a pendulum which beats seconds in various latitudes. Then by very delicate mathematical processes he can find with great exactness what would be the time of revolution of a small satellite at any given distance from the earth, and thus can get the earth-quotient.

But, as I have already pointed out, we must, in the case of the planets, find the quotient in question by means of the satellites; and it happens, fortunately, that the motions of these bodies are much less changed by the attraction of the sun than is the motion of the moon. Thus, when we make the computation for the outer satellite of Mars, we find the quotient to be $\frac{1}{3,085,000}$ that of the sun-quotient. Hence we conclude that the mass of Mars is $\frac{1}{3,085,000}$ that of the sun. By the corresponding quotient, the mass of Jupiter is found to be about $\frac{1}{1,047}$ that of the sun; Saturn, $\frac{1}{3,500}$; Uranus, $\frac{1}{22,700}$; Neptune, $\frac{1}{19,400}$.

I have set forth only the great principle on which the astronomer has proceeded for the purpose in question. The law of gravitation is at the bottom of all his work. The effects of this law require mathematical processes which it has taken more than two hundred years to bring to their present state, and which are still far from perfect. The measurement of the distance of a satellite is not a job to be done in an evening; it requires patient labor extending through months and years, and then is not as exact as the astronomer would wish. He does the best he can and must be satisfied with the result until he can devise an improvement on his work, which he is always trying to do, with varying success.

PART V

COMETS AND METEORS

I

COMETS differ from the heavenly bodies which we have hitherto studied in their peculiar aspects, their eccentric orbits, and the rarity of their appearance. Some mystery still surrounds the question of their constitution, but this does not detract from the interest of the phenomena which they present. A bright comet consists of three parts which, however, are not separate and distinct, but merge into each other.

First we have what, to the naked eye, appears to be a star. This is called the *nucleus* of the comet.

Surrounding the nucleus is a cloudy, nebulous mass, like a little bunch of fog, shading off very gradually toward the edge, so that we cannot exactly define its boundary. This is called the *coma* (Latin for hair). Nucleus and coma together are called the *head* of the comet, which looks like a star shining through a patch of mist or fog.

Stretching away from the comet is the tail, which may be of almost any length. In small comets the tail may be ever so short, while in the greatest it stretches over a long arc of the heavens. It is narrow and bright near the head of the comet, and grows wider and more diffuse as it recedes from the head. It is therefore always more or less fan-shaped. Toward the end it fades away so gradually that it is impossible to say how far the eye can trace it.

Comets differ enormously in brightness, and, notwithstanding the splendid aspect which the brighter ones assume, the great majority of these objects are quite invisible to the naked eye. There is, however, no broad distinction to be drawn between a telescopic comet and a bright one, there being a regular range of brightness from the faintest of these objects to the most brilliant. Sometimes a telescopic comet has no visible tail; this, however, is the case only when the object is extremely faint. Sometimes, also, the nucleus is almost wholly wanting. In such a case all that can be seen is a small foggy mass, like a very thin cloud, which may be a little brighter in the center.

From the historical records it would appear that from twenty to thirty comets visible to the naked eye generally appear in the course of a century. But when the telescope was employed in sweeping the heavens it was found that these objects are more numerous than had been supposed. Quite a number are now found every year by diligent observers. Doubtless the number depends very largely on accident, as well as on the skill applied in the search. Sometimes the same comet will be found independently by several observers. The credit is then given to the one who first accurately fixes the position of the comet at a given time, and telegraphs the fact to an observatory.

ORBITS OF COMETS

Soon after the invention of the telescope it was found that comets resemble the planets in moving in orbits around the sun. Sir Isaac Newton showed that their motions are ruled by the sun's gravitation in the same way as the motions of the planets. The great difference is that, instead of the orbits being nearly circular, like those of the planets, they are so elongated that, in most cases, it cannot be determined where the aphelion, or farther end, is. We shall enter into some explanations of the nature of cometary orbits, and the laws governing them.

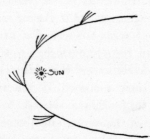

Fig. 37. *Parabolic Orbit of a Comet*

It was shown by Newton that a body moving under the influence of the sun's attraction always describes a conic section. This curve is of three kinds, an ellipse, a parabola, and a hyperbola. The first, as we all know, is a closed curve returning into itself. But the parabola and the hyperbola are not such; each of them extends out without end in two branches. In the parabola these two branches approach more nearly to having the same direction as we get out farther, but in the hyperbola they always diverge from each other.

Having these curves in mind, let us imagine the earth to leave us hanging in space at some point of its orbit, our planet pursuing its course without us, until, at the end of a year, it returns to pick us up again. During the interval of its absence we amuse ourselves by firing off balls to perform their revolutions around the sun like little planets. All the balls we send off with a velocity less than that of the earth, that is to say, less than eighteen and a half miles a second, will move around the sun in closed orbits, smaller than the orbit of the earth, no matter in what direction we send them. A very simple and curious law is that these orbits will always have the same period if the velocity is the same. All the balls sent with the velocity of the earth will require one year to make their revolution and will, therefore, come together, at the point from which they started, at the same moment. If the velocity exceeds eighteen and a half miles a second, the orbit will be larger than that of the earth, and the period of revolution will be longer the greater the velocity. With a speed exceeding about twenty-six miles a second, the attraction of the sun could never hold in the ball, which would fly away for good in one of the branches of a hyperbola. This would happen no matter in what direction we threw the object. There is, therefore, at every distance from the sun, a certain limiting velocity, and whenever it is exceeded, the comet will fly off from the sun never to return; while if it falls short, it will be sure to get back at some time.

The nearer we are to the sun, the greater is this limiting velocity. It varies inversely as the square root of the distance from the sun; hence, four times away from the sun, it is only half as great. The rule for finding the limiting velocity at any point in space is very simple. It is to take the speed of a planet passing through that point in a circular orbit, and multiply it by the square root of 2. This is 1.414. . . .

It follows that if the astronomer, by means of his observations, can find the velocity with which a comet is passing a known point of its orbit, he can determine the distance to which it will fly from the sun and the period of its return. By a careful comparison of observations made during the whole period of visibility of the comet he can generally reach a definite conclusion on the subject.

It is a fact that no comet has yet been seen whose speed certainly exceeds the limit which we have described. It is true that, in many cases, a slight excess has been calculated from the observations, but this excess is no greater than might result from the necessary errors of observations on bodies of this kind. Commonly the speed is so near the limit that it is impossible to say whether it exceeds it or not. It is then certain that the comet will fly out to an immense distance, not returning for hundreds, thousands, or tens of thousands of years. There are also cases in which the speed of the comet is found to be less than the limit by a considerable amount. Such comets complete their revolutions in shorter periods and are called *periodic comets*.

So far as we know, the history of the motion of the large majority of the comets is this. They appear to us as if falling toward the sun from some great distance, we know not what. If a comet is directed exactly toward the sun, it will fall into it, but this is a case which has not been known to occur and which, for reasons to be explained later, cannot be expected ever to occur.

As it approaches the sun, the comet acquires greater and greater velocity, speeds around the central body in a great curve, and, by the centrifugal force thus generated, flies off again, returning to the abyss of space nearly in the direction from which it came.

Owing to the faintness of these objects they are visible, even in powerful telescopes, only in that part of the orbit which is comparatively near the sun. This is what makes it so difficult in many cases to determine the exact period of a comet which has been seen only once.

HALLEY'S COMET

The first of these objects which was found to return in a regular period is celebrated in the history of astronomy under the name of Halley's comet. It appeared in August, 1682, and was observed for about a month, when it disappeared from view. Halley was able, from the observations made upon it, to compute the elements of the orbit. He found that it followed the same specifications as the orbit of a bright comet observed by Kepler in 1607.

It did not seem at all likely that two comets should move precisely in the same orbit. Halley therefore judged that the real orbit was an ellipse, and that the comet had a period of about seventy-five years. If this were the case, it should have been visible at intervals of about seventy-five years in the past.

So he subtracted this period from the several dates in order to determine whether any comets were recorded. Subtracting seventy-five from 1607 we have 1532. He found that a comet had actually appeared

FIG. 38.—*Halley's Comet in 1910. (From photo-graph at Yerkes Observatory.)*

in 1531, which he had reason to believe was moving in the same orbit. Again subtracting seventy-five from this year we have the year 1456. A comet really did appear in 1456, which spread such horror throughout Christendom that Pope Calixtus III ordered prayers to be offered for protection against the comet as well as against the Turks, who were at war against Europe. It is probable that the myth of "the Pope's Bull against the comet" refers to this circumstance.

Other possible appearances of the comet were found in past history, but Halley was not able to identify the comet with exactness, owing to the absence of any precise description of the body. But the four well-observed dates, 1456, 1531, 1607, and 1682, afforded ample ground for predicting that the comet would again return to the sun about 1758. Clairaut, one of the most eminent mathematicians then in France, was able to calculate what effect would be produced by the action of Jupiter and Saturn on the period of the comet. He found that this action would so delay its return that it would not reach perihelion until the spring of 1759. It appeared according to the prediction, and actually passed perihelion on March twelfth of that year.

Halley's comet passed perihelion next in November, 1835, and again in May, 1910. At its latest appearance it presented a beautiful sight in the eastern sky before dawn early in May. On May 19, the comet's head passed directly between the earth and the sun, and two days later its tail may well have brushed the earth. Nothing could be observed of either occurrence. By July, 1911, the comet had receded so far that it faded from view even with the telescope. It is now beyond Neptune's orbit, where it will remain for more than 30 years, passing the aphelion point in 1948. Halley's comet will return to perihelion in 1985, when it will doubtless be again a spectacular object to the unaided eye.

COMETS WHICH HAVE DISAPPEARED

A comet of unusual interest was discovered by the French astronomer Lexell, in June, 1770. The object soon became visible to the naked eye. It was moving in an elliptical orbit, with a period of only about six years. Its return was, therefore, confidently predicted, but it never reappeared. The cause was, however, speedily discovered. When it returned at the end of six years, it was on the opposite side of the sun, and therefore could not be seen. Passing out to complete its revolution, it must have gone into the immediate neighborhood of the planet Jupiter, whose powerful attraction started the comet off into some new orbit, so that it never again came within reach of the telescope. This, also, explained why the comet had not been seen before. Three years before Lexell found it, it had come from the neighborhood of the planet Jupiter, which had thrown it into an orbit different from its former one. Thus the giant planet of our system had, so to speak, given the comet a pull about 1767 so that it should pass into the immediate neighborhood of the sun, and having allowed it to make two revolutions around the sun, again encountered it in 1779, and gave it a new swing off, no one knows where. Since that time twenty or thirty comets, found to be periodic, have been observed, most, but not all of them, at two or more returns.

Comets are subject to dissolution and decay. An interesting case of apparently complete disintegration is that of Biela's comet. This comet was first observed in 1772, but was not known to be periodic. It was again seen in 1805, and again the astronomer did not notice the identity of the orbit in which it was moving with that of the comet of 1772. In 1826 it was discovered a third time, and now the computation of the orbit by the improved methods established its identity with the former comets. The time of revolution was fixed at six and two thirds years. It should, therefore, appear in 1832 and 1839. But on these returns the earth was not in a position to admit of its being seen. Toward the end of 1845 it again appeared and was observed in November and December. In January, 1846, as it came nearer to the earth and sun, it was found to have separated into two distinct bodies. At first the smaller of these was quite faint, but it seemed to increase in brightness until it became equal to the other.

The next return was in 1852. The two bodies were then found to be far more widely separated than before. In 1846 their distance apart was about two hundred thousand miles; in 1852 more than a million miles. The last observations were made in September, 1852. Although since that time the comet should have completed seven revolutions, it has never again been seen. From the former returns it was possible to compute with a good deal of precision the position where it should appear, and from its nonappearance we might conclude that it has been completely disintegrated. We shall, in the next chapter, learn a little more about the matter which composed it.

Two or three comets have disappeared in the same way. They were observed for one or more revolutions, growing fainter and more attenuated on each occasion, and finally became completely invisible.

ENCKE'S COMET

Of the periodic comets the one that is most frequently and regularly observed bears the name of Encke, the German astronomer who first accurately determined its motion. Its first discovery was made in 1786, but, as was often the case then, its orbit could not at first be determined. It was again seen in 1795 by Miss Caroline Herschel. It was found again in 1805 and 1818. Not until the latter date was the accurate orbit determined, and then the periodic character of the comet and its identity with the comet observed in previous years was established.

Encke now found the period to be about three years and one hundred and ten days, varying a little according to the attraction of the planets, especially of Jupiter. In recent times it has been observed somewhere at almost every return. The return in 1928 was the thirty-seventh to be recorded.

What has given this comet its celebrity is the fact that its orbit became smaller continually for many years, until its mean distance from the sun was reduced by more than a quarter of a million miles. The theory has been proposed that its motion was being resisted by some medium surrounding the sun. A number of astronomers have investigated this subject on the various returns of the comet. Sometimes there appears to be evidence of a retardation from one return to the next, and sometimes not.

CAPTURE OF COMETS BY JUPITER

A remarkable case, in which a new comet was made a member of the solar system, occurred in the years 1886-1889. In the latter year a comet was observed by Brooks, which proved to be revolving in an orbit with a period of only seven years. As the comet was quite bright, the question arose why it had never been observed before. This question was soon answered by the discovery that in the year 1886 the comet had passed close to Jupiter. The attraction of the planet had so changed its course as to throw the comet into the orbit which it now describes. Other periodic comets pass so near to Jupiter that there is little doubt that they were captured in this way.

The question therefore arises whether this may not be true of all comets whose periods are fairly short. This question must be answered in the negative, because Halley's comet does not pass near any planet. The same is true of Encke's comet, which does not come near enough to the orbit of Jupiter to have been drawn into its present orbit, although, when its orbit was larger, it may well have done so.

WHENCE COME COMETS?

It was supposed, until a recent time, that comets might come into the solar system from the vast spaces between the stars. This view, however, seems to be set aside by the fact that no comet has been proved to move with a much higher speed than it would get by falling to the sun from a distance, which, though far outside the orbit of the most remote planet, is much less than the distance of the stars. We shall see hereafter that the sun itself is in motion through space. Even if we grant that comets come from space far outside the solar system, the fact that we have just cited still shows that they partook of the motion of the sun and solar system through space while they were still outside that system.

The view which now seems established by a study of the whole subject is that these objects have their regular orbits, differing from those of the planets in their great eccentricities. Their periods of revolution are generally thousands, and sometimes tens of thousands, and even hundreds of thousands of years. During this long interval they fly out to an enormous distance beyond the confines of the planetary system. If, as they return to the sun, they chance to pass very near a planet, two things may happen: Either the comet may be given an additional swing that will accelerate its speed, throw it out to a greater distance than it ever had before or possibly to a distance from which it can never return, or the speed may be retarded and the comet made to move in a smaller orbit. Thus we have comets of so many different periods. We conclude that the comets we see are, at present, members of the solar system. It has been suggested, and it is not impossible, that our supply of comets was taken on at some time

in the remote past when the sun passed through a cosmic dust-cloud—one of the dark nebulæ.

BRILLIANT COMETS

The very bright comets which appear from time to
time are of the greatest interest to every beholder. It
is purely a matter of chance, so far as our knowledge
extends, when one will appear. Of what are called great
comets, there were five or six during the nineteenth
century. The most remarkable and brilliant of all appeared in 1858, and bears the name of the Italian astronomer Donati, its discoverer. Its history will show
the changes through which such a body goes. The
comet was first seen on June 2, but was then only a
faint nebulosity, visible in the telescope like a minute
white cloud in the heavens. No tail was then visible,
nor was there the slightest indication of what the little
cloud would grow into, until the middle of August.
Then a small tail began to form. Early in September
the object became visible to the naked eye. From that
time it increased at an extraordinary rate, growing
larger and more conspicuous night after night. It
seemed to move but little for the period of a whole
month, floating in the western sky night after night.
It attained its greatest brilliancy about October 10.
Careful drawings of it were made from time to time
by George P. Bond, of the Harvard Observatory. We
give two of these, one a naked eye view, the other a
telescopic one showing what the head of the comet
looked like. After October 10 it rapidly faded away. It
soon travelled toward the south, and passed below our

horizon, but was followed by observers in the southern hemisphere until March, 1859.

Before the comet had passed out of sight, computers began to calculate its orbit. It was soon found not to move in an exact parabola, but in a very elongated ellipse. The period was not far from nineteen hundred years, but may have been a hundred years more or less than this. It must therefore have been visible at its preceding return sometime in the first century before Christ, but there is no record by which it could be identified. It may be expected again in the thirty-eighth or thirty-ninth century.

A very remarkable case of several comets moving in very nearly the same orbit is afforded by the comets of 1843, 1880, and 1882. The first of these was one of the most memorable comets on record. It passed so near the sun as almost to graze the surface; in fact, it must have passed quite through the outer portions of the solar corona. It came into view with remarkable suddenness in the neighborhood of the sun, about the end of February. It was visible in full daylight. By a singular coincidence it appeared shortly after a prediction that the end of the world was to come in the year 1843. Those who had been alarmed by this prediction saw in the comet an omen of the approaching catastrophe.

The comet disappeared from view in April, so that the time of observation was rather short. The period of revolution now became a subject of interest. It was found, however, that its orbit did not differ sensibly from the parabola. But the time of observation was so brief that any estimate of the period would be somewhat uncertain. All that could be said was that the comet would not return for several centuries.

Great, therefore, was the surprise when, thirty-seven years later, a comet was seen by observers in the southern hemisphere and found to be moving in almost the same orbit. The first sign which it gave of its approach was its long tail rising above the horizon. This was seen in the Argentine Republic, at the Cape of Good Hope, and in Australia. Not until the fourth of February did the head become visible. It swept around the sun, again passed to the south, and disappeared without observers in the northern hemisphere seeing it.

The question now arose whether this could possibly be the same comet that had appeared in 1843. Previously it had been supposed that when two such bodies move in the same orbit with a long interval between they must be the same. In the present case, however, the hypothesis of identity seemed to be incompatible with the observations. The question was set at rest by the appearance, in 1882, of a third comet moving in about the same orbit. This certainly could not be a return of the comet which had appeared a little more than two years before. The remarkable spectacle was therefore offered of three bright comets all moving in the same orbit at unequal intervals of time. In this group we must include also two comets which appeared in 1668 and 1887.

Probably they are five parts of a single comet which was disrupted near perihelion by the sun's attraction. Indeed, the nucleus of one of the group, the great September comet of 1882, broke into four parts soon after its perihelion passage. The separate parts will return, about a century apart, as four distinct comets having periods of from 660 to 960 years.

It seems probable that the nucleus of a comet is largely a collection of meteoric matter, of sizes ranging anywhere from that of grains of sand to masses as large as the meteorites which sometimes fall from the sky. The question then is to explain how the parts are kept together through so many revolutions of the comet. The changes of shape which the nucleus often undergoes as it is passing near to the sun seem to show that this hypothesis is near the truth.

The spectra of those comets whose light has been thus analyzed show clearly that this light is not merely reflected sunlight. The principal feature is three bright bands, which bear a striking resemblance to those given by the compounds of carbon and hydrogen. It is the spectrum of the glowing gas which enters also into the constitution of the comet.

In most cases, at least, it is not the sun's heat which causes the gas to glow. It is some other action of the sun, analogous perhaps to that which causes the auroral light in our upper atmosphere, and which lights up the distant nebulæ.

It seems certain that the matter of which a bright comet is composed is volatile. When a bright comet is carefully scrutinized with a telescope, masses of vapor can be seen from time to time slowly rising from its head in the direction of the sun, then spreading out and moving away from the sun so as to form the tail. The latter is not an appendage which the comet carries, as animals carry their tails, but is like a stream of smoke issuing from a chimney.

It frequently happens that when a comet is first discovered it has no tail at all. The tail begins to form when the sun is approached. The nearer the comet approaches the sun, and the greater the heat to which it is exposed, the more rapidly the tail develops. The material of which the tail is composed moves rapidly outward. Apparently, it is vigorously repelled by the sun's radiation. Thus the comet's tail is directed away from the sun.

II

METEORS

EVERY reader of this book must frequently have seen what is familiarly called a "shooting star"—an object like a star, which darts through the heavens and then disappears. These objects are, in astronomy, called by the generic name of *meteors*. They are of every degree of brightness, but the brighter they are, the more rarely they appear. One who is out much at night will seldom pass a year without seeing such a meteor of striking brilliancy. Occasionally he may see one that illuminates the whole sky with its light.

On almost any clear night in the year a watcher can see three or four or even more meteors in the course of an hour. Sometimes, however, they are vastly more numerous, for example, between the tenth and fifteenth of August, more and brighter ones than usual will be seen. On a number of occasions in history they have coursed the heavens in such numbers as to fill the beholders with surprise and terror. There were remarkable cases of this kind in 1799, 1833, and 1866–1867. In the latter years especially, the Negroes of the South were so terrified that the recollection of the phenomenon is brought down by tradition to the present day.

METEORS AND METEORITES

The cause of meteors was unknown until after the beginning of the nineteenth century. Besides the known objects of the solar system—planets, satellites, and comets—there are, coursing through space, and revolving around the sun, countless millions of meteors too small to be seen with the most powerful telescope. Quite likely the greater number of these objects are scarcely larger than pebbles, or even grains of sand. The earth, in its course around the sun, is continually encountering them. One in the line of motion of the earth may have a velocity amounting to many miles a second; perhaps ten, twenty, thirty, or even forty. Meeting the atmosphere with this immense velocity, the body is immediately heated to so high a temperature that its substance dissolves away with a brilliant effusion of light, no matter how solid it may be. What we see is the course of a particle thus burning away as it darts through the rare regions of the upper atmosphere.

Of course, a meteor will appear brighter and last longer the larger and solider it is. Sometimes it is so large and solid that it comes within a few miles of the earth before being finally melted and dissolved away. Then, the people in the region over which it is passing see a remarkably bright meteor. In such a case it frequently happens that in a few minutes after the meteor has passed a loud explosion, like the firing of a cannon, is heard coming from the region through which it passed. This arises from the concussion of the air compressed by the rapid flight.

Sometimes the mass is so large that it reaches the earth without being melted or evaporated. Then we have the fall of a meteorite, as it is called, which occurs many times a year in some part or another of the world.

METEORIC SHOWERS

The greatest discovery of our times on the subject of meteors is connected with the meteoric showers already referred to, which occur at certain seasons of the year. Remarkable showers have occurred near the middle of November; the meteors of the shower are called *Leonids*, because their lines of apparent motion all diverge from the constellation Leo. It was found by historical research that this shower has occurred at intervals of about one third of a century for at least thirteen hundred years. The earliest account is the following from an Arabian writer:

In the year 599, on the last day of Moharren, stars shot hither and thither, and flew against each other like a swarm of locusts; people were thrown into consternation and made supplication to the Most High; there was never the like seen except on the coming of the messenger of God; on whom be benediction and peace.

The first well-described shower of this class occurred on November 12, 1799. It was seen by Humboldt, then on the Andes. He seems to have considered it as a very remarkable display, but made no exact investigation as to its cause.

The next recurrence was in 1833. The astronomer Olbers suggested that the shower had a period of thirty-four years, and predicted a possible return in 1867, which actually appeared, and, in 1866 also. In 1866 and 1867 the observations were more carefully made than ever before, and led to the discovery of the relation between meteors and comets. To explain this we must define the radiant point of meteors.

It is found that if, during a meteoric shower, we mark the course of each meteor by a line on the celestial sphere, and continue these lines backward, we shall find that they all meet at a certain point in the heavens. In the case of the November meteors this point is in the contellation Leo; in the August meteors it is in Perseus. It is called the *radiant* of the shower. The lines in which the meteors move are the same as if they were all shot out from this one point, but it must not be supposed that the meteors are actually seen at this point; they may begin to show themselves at any distance from it less than ninety degrees; but when they are seen they are moving from the point. This shows that the meteors are all moving in parallel lines when they encounter our atmosphere. The radiant point is what, in perspective, is called the vanishing point.

CONNECTION OF COMETS AND METEORS

The period of the November meteors, thirty-three years, being known, and the exact position of the radiant point determined, it became possible to calculate the orbit of these objects. This was done by Leverrier soon after the shower of 1866. Now it happened that, in December, 1865, a comet appeared which passed its perihelion in January, 1866. The study of its motion showed that its period was about thirty-three years. This orbit was computed by Oppolzer, who published it without noticing its resemblance to that of the meteors. Then it was noticed by Schiaparelli that there was an almost perfect resemblance between the orbit of Oppolzer's comet and the Leverrier orbit of the November meteors. So near together were they that no doubt could be felt that the two orbits were identical. The evident fact was that the bodies which produced these November meteors were following the comet in its orbit. It was therefore concluded that these objects had originally formed part of the comet and had gradually separated from it. When a comet is disintegrated in the manner described in the last chapter, those portions of its mass which are not completely dissipated continue to revolve around the sun as minute particles, which get gradually separated from each other in consequence of there being no sufficient bond of attraction, but they still follow each other in line in nearly the same orbit.

The same thing was found to be true of the August meteors. They move in an orbit very near to that of a comet observed in 1862. The period of this comet is 123 years.

The third remarkable case of this kind occurred in 1872. We have already spoken of the disappearance of Biela's comet. It happens that the orbit of this body nearly intersected that of the earth at the point which the latter passes toward the end of November. From the observed period of this comet it should have passed this point about the first of September, 1872, between two and three months before the passage of the earth through the same point. From the analogy of the other cases it was therefore judged that there would be a meteoric shower on the evening of November 27, 1872, and that the radiant point would be in the constellation Andromeda. This prediction was fulfilled in every respect. The *Andromedes*, as these meteors are called, produced some fine showers; but since 1899, only a few of these meteors have been seen.

The comet of 1866 should have reappeared sometime during the years 1898–1900, but it was not seen. Perhaps it was missed, not because of its complete disintegration, but because it happened to pass its perihelion at a time when the earth was too far away to admit of the comet being visible. Moreover, the meteors themselves, a shower of which was expected in 1899–1900, did not reappear in great numbers at either date. The probable reason for this is that the swarm was deflected from its course by the attraction of the planets, which continually changes the orbit of every object of this kind.

One might be tempted to conclude that the countless thousands of comets which in time past have coursed around the sun, have left behind minute fragments of their mass, which follow in their orbits like stragglers from an army, and that when the earth encounters a swarm of these fragments a meteoric shower is produced. But it is still an open question, and it is certainly doubtful that all these meteoric particles can be fragments of comets. The velocities of meteors as they enter the atmosphere often exceed the parabolic limit described in the last chapter. These, it would seem, must be wanderers through the infinite stellar spaces, having no connection with our system.

THE ZODIACAL LIGHT

This is a very soft, faint light, surrounding the sun, extending out to about the orbit of the earth, and lying nearly in the plane of the ecliptic. In tropical latitudes it may be seen on any clear evening about an hour or less after sunset. In our latitudes it is best seen in the evening in the spring, when, about an hour and a half after sunset, it may always be seen in the west and southwest, extending upward toward the Pleiades. It is best seen at this season because it is symmetrical with the ecliptic, and therefore stands at a greater angle with the horizon then than at other seasons. In autumn it may be seen in the morning before daybreak, rising from the east and extending toward the south.

Immediately opposite the sun there is always a faint light, to which the term *Gegenschein* is applied. This is a German word, of which the best English equivalent is *counter-glow*. The light is so faint that it can be seen only under the most favorable conditions. When it falls in the Milky Way the light of that body is sufficient to drown it out, as is that of the moon.

The Gegenschein passes through the Milky Way in June and December of each year, and can therefore not be seen during these months. Nor is it likely to be seen during the first part of January or July. At other times it must be looked for when the sun is considerably below the horizon, the sky perfectly clear, and the moon not in sight. It may then be seen as an extremely faint impression of light, to which no exact outline can be assigned. The observer will find it by sweeping his eye over the region of the spot exactly opposite the sun.

It is generally believed that the zodiacal light is caused by the reflection of the light of the sun from a swarm of very minute bodies, perhaps in the nature of meteors, continually revolving around it. We might naturally attribute the Gegenschein to the same cause, and dynamical reasons have been assigned for the congregating of meteoric material opposite the sun. It has been suggested also that the earth has a tail, like a comet, and that the Gegenschein is simply this tail seen endwise.

Part VI
THE STARS

I

HAVING completed our survey of that small section of the universe in which we have our dwelling, we turn to more distant parts of space occupied by the thousands of stars which ornament our skies.

The whole number of stars in the heavens which can be seen by the average eye is between five and six thousand. Of these only a half can be above the horizon at one time; and of this half a great number will be so near the horizon as to be obscured by intervening parts of the landscape and by the greater thickness of atmosphere in that direction. The number which can be readily seen by the average eye on a clear, moonless evening is between fifteen hundred and two thousand. Stars visible to the naked eye are called *lucid stars*, to distinguish them from the vast multitude of stars which the telescope brings into view.

As we watch the stars twinkling in the evening sky we can easily lose sight of the fact that they are not all equally remote, for they seem to be at the same distance. We can imagine that they are set on the inner surface of a great sphere which completely encloses the earth. By the turning of this sphere on its inclined axis the stars are brought into view in the east and carried out of sight in the west. But the stars in the north circle around the pole without setting, for observers in the latitudes of the United States, while other stars wheel around the south pole of the heavens, invisible to us, without ever coming into view. The westward rotation of the starry sphere, once around in a sidereal day, proceeds therefore at the rate of a degree in a little less than four minutes.

As everyone knows, it is the earth's eastward rotation on its axis that causes the celestial scenery to circle westward daily. Meanwhile, in consequence of the earth's revolution around the sun, the sun appears to move slowly eastward among the stars, slightly less than one degree in a day, completing its circuit along the ecliptic in the course of a year. These effects of the earth's motions have been described in a previous chapter.

Owing to the sun's eastward displacement, a day by the stars, the sidereal day, very nearly, which is the actual period of the earth's rotation is nearly four minutes shorter than a day by the sun. Each night a star rises nearly four minutes earlier than on the previous night; and at the same hour it is a degree farther west. As the seasons go around, therefore, all the stars that rise and set pass in review across the evening sky.

The stars are not scattered uniformly over the sky. They are assembled in groups; some of them, such as the Great Dipper and the Square of Pegasus, are so striking that once noticed they are not likely to be forgotten. Ancient peoples were as familiar with the conspicuous groups of stars as we are. The face of the sky has changed very little in a few thousand years. And they named these groups. So began the constellations.

Our constellations have descended to us, with some alterations and additions, from the early Greeks who probably learned them from the people of Mesopotamia. As early as the ninth century B. C. Homer mentioned the Great Bear, Orion, and some other familiar configurations. The earliest fairly complete account of the ancient constellations, nearly fifty in all, is to be found in the *Phenomena* which Aratus, poet laureate of the king of Macedonia, wrote about 270 B. C. Their names are those of mythological heroes and animals, and they are associated with many familiar stories.

Eighty-eight constellations are recognized to-day, of which eighteen around the south celestial pole never rise above the horizon in middle northern latitudes. The additions to the original list were designed to fill vacant places between the ancient constellations, and also the area around the south celestial pole which was invisible to the Greeks.

Astronomers have retained, in the Latin form, the old names of the constellations, but the figures of the heroes and animals have almost entirely disappeared in the modern maps. For practical purposes, the constellations have become regions of the sky containing the various groups of stars, and set off by arbitrary boundary lines, as our states are bounded. By international agreement the boundary lines of the constellations are parallel and perpendicular to the celestial equator. All stars within the boundaries of a particular constellation are members of it; and whenever a planet or the sun or moon is included, it is said to be in the constellation.

Since the moon and the planets, in general, as well

as the sun, do not stray far from the ecliptic, they are usually associated with the twelve constellations of the zodiac, which lie along the ecliptic. Their names are: Aries, Taurus, Gemini, Cancer, Leo, Virgo, Libra, Scorpio, Sagittarius, Capricornus, Aquarius, and Pisces. The zodiac is the band around the heavens sixteen degrees wide through which the ecliptic runs centrally. It is divided into twelve equal parts, the signs of the zodiac, which are marked off eastward from the vernal equinox. They are named after the twelve constellations. Two thousand years ago, each sign included its own constellation. Owing to precession, which we have already described, the signs of the zodiac have now shifted westward, so that they no longer coincide with the constellations of the same name.

This chapter is intended to assist the reader in recognizing the principal constellations which are visible in the course of the year in the latitudes of the United States. Most of them contain characteristic configurations of stars, such as a square, a cross, or a dipper figure, easy to identify in the sky from the descriptions and the maps which accompany them. Each season brings its own display of constellations into the evening skies. It does not matter with what season we begin. Anyone who makes a beginning in the learning of the constellations is likely to continue, as the familiar groups disappear in the west and new ones to be learned appear in the east, until the circle of the year is completed.

It is convenient for our purpose to divide the visible portion of the heavens into five regions. First, we have the northern constellations which circle around the celestial pole without setting, and are therefore generally in view throughout the year in middle northern latitudes. The remaining regions contain the constellations which rise and set, and cross generally south of the zenith. With each of the four seasons we here identify those constellations which are crossing the celestial meridian at 9 o'clock in the evening during that season. In the maps we show only the brighter stars, in general, in order to avoid confusion; and for the same reason we omit the boundary lines.

THE NORTHERN CONSTELLATIONS

The map which shows the constellations of the northern sky is found in the first part of the book, in Figure 2. The center of the map is the north celestial pole around which the stars appear to wheel in the counter clockwise direction, once around in four minutes less than a day. From night to night at the same hour they advance, therefore, about a degree. To make the map agree with the sky at nine o'clock in the evening, turn it so that the month appears at the top.

First find *Ursa Major*, the Great Bear, whose bright stars form the familiar Dipper. This group can be found at any time of the year except perhaps in autumn when it is near the horizon. Notice the two stars which form the forward side of the bowl of the dipper. They are the *Pointers*, so named because they point toward the pole star. This star, Polaris, is near the center of the map, within about a degree of the celestial pole, and therefore marking its place in the sky approximately.

The pole star belongs to the constellation *Ursa Minor*, the Lesser Bear, more often known as the Small Dipper. It marks the end of the handle of this dipper, the rest of which is rather faint with the exception of the two stars on the forward side of the bowl. These two are known as the Guardians of the pole, because they march around it incessantly.

If the pointer stars are not in sight, the pole star can be found by looking directly north, and as high above the horizon as the number of degrees in the latitude of the place of observation. Thus in latitude 45° the pole star is halfway from the horizon to the zenith.

On the opposite side of the pole from the Great Dipper, and at about the same distance, is the Chair of *Cassiopeia*. Five bright stars form the letter W, or M. Two fainter ones complete the chair; it has a very crooked back, and could be made more comfortable by a cushion in the hollow.

Preceding Cassiopeia in the daily circuit around the pole we find *Cepheus*. To some people it resembles a church spire, having its apex near the pole. In advance of Cepheus, nearly halfway around the pole to the Great Dipper, is the V-shaped head of *Draco*. The body of the dragon, composed of rather faint stars, can be followed from the map. It winds around the north pole of the ecliptic, the point about two thirds of the way from Polaris to the head of the dragon. This point, unmarked by a bright star, is the center around which the north celestial pole is very slowly circling in consequence of the earth's precessional motion.

These are the five conspicuous constellations of the

northern heavens. Having identified them, we face toward the south, selecting the map for the season in which we are observing. Suppose that it is autumn.

THE AUTUMN CONSTELLATIONS

The map in Figure 39 shows the principal constellations which ornament the southern skies during the autumn. Vertically below the name of the month we find those groups that are crossing the celestial meridian at nine o'clock in the evening during that month, extending from the zenith, near the top of the map, to the south point of the horizon, near the bottom. The horizontal line through the middle of the map is part of the celestial equator. The slanting line represents part of the ecliptic.

The square of *Pegasus* is the easily recognized landmark of the autumn skies. Early in the season the square appears directly in the east. By the first of November, it has advanced to a place high up in the south at nine o'clock. Fifteen degrees on a side, the square is formed by four stars of the second magnitude. Northeast from the northeast corner of the square is the great nebula of *Andromeda*. Brightest of the great spirals which lie far beyond the Milky Way, and which will be described later, it appears to the naked eye as an elongated, foggy patch of light. If we imagine the square of Pegasus to be the bowl of a very large dipper, the handle, toward the northeast, is formed by the bright stars of Andromeda. The end star in the handle, however, is Alpha Persei.

Perseus stands in the Milky Way, an arrowhead of

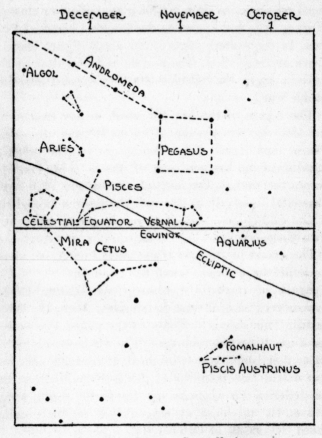

Fig. 39. *Autumn Constellations*

stars pointing toward Cassiopeia. Midway between the two we observe a cloudy patch which is resolved by a small telescope, or even a field glass, into two clusters of stars. It is well known as the Double Cluster of Perseus. In the western barb of the arrow figure there is a row of three stars. The middle and brightest of the three is Algol, the "Demon Star," a typical eclipsing double star.

The region of the heavens which we are examining includes the three zodiacal constellations, *Aquarius*, *Pisces*, and *Aries*. The ecliptic crosses the celestial equator in the western part of Pisces. This crossing point, the vernal equinox, where the sun stands on March 21, is nearly in line with the eastern side of the square of Pegasus, and about one length to the south. Two thousand years ago, this equinox was northeast of its present position, in the constellation Aries, whose principal stars form a small flat triangle.

South of Pisces is the large constellation *Cetus*, famous because of its red variable star Mira, the Wonderful. This star is invisible to the naked eye except for a month or two each year. The whole region of the autumn constellations is subdued. It contains only one star of the first magnitude; this is Fomalhaut, in the constellation *Piscis Austrinus*, far to the south, which crosses the meridian at nine o'clock in the evening about the middle of October.

THE WINTER CONSTELLATIONS

The constellations of winter (Figure 40) are the brightest in the heavens. Their brilliant stars sparkle

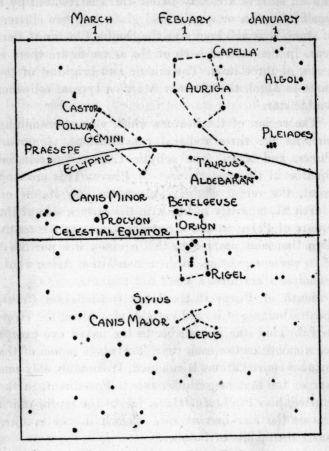

FIG. 40. *Winter Constellations*

and splinter into prismatic colors through the long cold nights, as if to compensate for the deficiencies of the sun during this season.

Orion is brightest of all the constellations. Four stars mark the corners of a rectangle, upended as we see it in the south. The great red star Betelgeuse is located in the upper east corner, the blue Rigel in the lower west. Three bright stars in line near the center of the rectangle form the belt of the hero, while three fainter ones below ornament his sword. The middle of the fainter trio is really not a star at all, but one of the finest of the nebulæ, the great nebula in Orion, a very remarkable sight with the telescope.

The line of Orion's belt directs the eye southward to Sirius, the Dog Star, the brightest of all the stars. It is in the constellation *Canis Major*, the Great Dog. East of Orion, and forming an equilateral triangle with Sirius and Betelgeuse, we find the first magnitude star Procyon, in the small constellation *Canis Minor*, the Little Dog.

Following the line of Orion's belt upward, we come to the V-shaped cluster of the Hyades, and, a little way beyond, to the more compact cluster of the Pleiades, or the "seven sisters." Both are examples of open star clusters which will be described later. The Hyades mark the head of *Taurus*, the Bull. The bright red star Aldebaran forms his eye, while two conspicuous stars farther east are at the tips of his horns. Above these two stars we find the constellation *Auriga* whose great yellow star Capella is one of the three brightest in the northern celestial hemisphere.

Taurus, Gemini, and Cancer are the three zodiacal

constellations along the course of the ecliptic in this region of the heavens. This part of the ecliptic is the farthest north.

Gemini, the Heavenly Twins, has the form of a long rectangle, with the bright stars Castor and Pollux at its eastern end. It was in this constellation that the planet Pluto was discovered, in 1930. *Cancer*, the Crab, whose name is given to our northern tropic, is a rather faint constellation. Its most interesting feature is the Praesepe cluster, which appears as a hazy spot to the naked eye. A field glass shows it as an open cluster of stars.

This region of the winter constellations includes a part of the Milky Way, which adds to the splendor of the starry scenery on a very clear night, although it is not so brilliant and spectacular as the part that we see in the summer.

THE SPRING CONSTELLATIONS

As the brilliant configurations of the winter disappear below the horizon, they are replaced by the somewhat less spectacular star groups of the spring (Figure 41). *Leo* is the dominant constellation of this region of the heavens. Its appearance in the east in the early evening is to many people the harbinger of approaching spring. During April, it is high in the southern sky at nine o'clock in the evening.

Leo is recognized by its sickle of seven stars; the brightest one of the group, at the end of the handle of the sickle is Regulus, a star of the first magnitude. East of the sickle is a right triangle, and farthest east

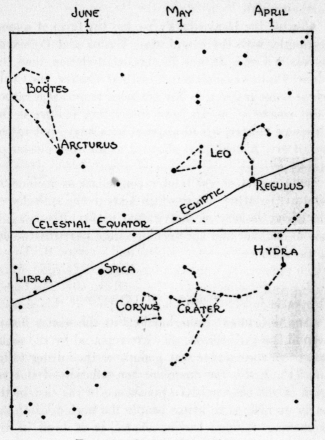

FIG. 41. *Spring Constellations*

in the triangle is Denebola. There are some who imagine a lion outlined by the stars of this constellation.

A line from Denebola to the star at the end of the
handle of the Great Dipper passes through two incon-
spicuous constellations, *Coma Berenices* and *Canes
Venatici.* The former contains a star cluster, some of
whose stars can be discerned with the naked eye. This
part of the heavens is of great interest to the observer
with a large telescope, because it is thickly populated
by spiral nebulæ and other very remote systems external to our own.

The longest constellation of all, *Hydra,* stretches
across the southern skies of spring as an irregular line
of stars, from a point south of Cancer nearly to Scorpio. Near the middle of its course we find two constellations of considerable interest; they are *Crater,* the
Cup, which resembles a goblet, and *Corvus,* the Crow,
which appears as a quadrilateral of fairly bright stars.

Return for a moment to the northern sky. The Great
Dipper is inverted and above the pole at this season.
Follow the curve of the handle through the end star
around toward the south. Presently a very bright
orange star is encountered, and at an equal distance beyond along the curve a blue star somewhat less brilliant. The first star is Arcturus, in *Boötes;* the second
is Spica, in *Virgo.* Boötes has the form of a kite, with
Arcturus at the point where the tail is attached.

Virgo is a large constellation of the zodiac whose
stars form no very definite figure by which it may be
remembered. Spica completes an equilateral triangle,
with Arcturus and Denebola at the other vertices. A
line from Spica to Regulus represents very nearly the

course of the ecliptic in this region of the heavens. And a point two fifths of the way along this line marks approximately the autumnal equinox where the sun, on September 23, crosses the celestial equator.

THE SUMMER CONSTELLATIONS

Celestial scenery of the greatest variety and interest is on display during the summer months (Figure 42). Immediately east of the kite of Boötes, *Corona*, the Northern Crown, is readily recognized. It is a semicircle of stars with the open part toward the north.

As far again to the east is the part of *Hercules* that appears to some observers like a butterfly with outstretched wings. Here, barely visible to the naked eye, the globular cluster in Hercules is one of the showpieces with the telescope. This great ball of stars is the most superb example of its class that is visible in northern latitudes. The eastern part of Hercules contains the solar apex, the point toward which the whole solar system is moving with relation to the stars around us.

East of Hercules we find *Lyra* with its brilliant blue star Vega. Still farther east we come to the Northern Cross with its principal axis directed along the Milky Way. It is *Cygnus*, the Swan, whose brightest star, Deneb, marks the top of the cross. Here the Milky Way divides into two parallel streams. Let us follow its course toward the south.

We pass by two little constellations, *Sagitta*, the Arrow, and *Delphinus*, the Dolphin, often called "Job's Coffin." Next comes the larger constellation *Aquila*, the Eagle. Its brightest star Altair is in a line between two

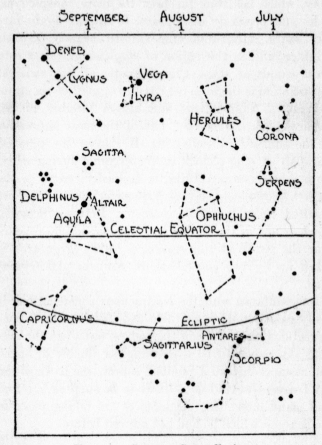

Fig. 42. *Summer Constellations*

fainter stars. Here the western branch of the Milky
Way, which has thus far been the more conspicuous,
fades and presently disappears, to appear again farther south. Meanwhile, the eastern branch becomes
brighter, and in the region of *Sagittarius* forms into
great clouds of stars. Characteristic of this zodiacal
constellation is the inverted "Milk Dipper" of six stars.

West of Saggittarius and also a member of the
zodiacal group, *Scorpio* is one of the most impressive
of the summer constellations. It crosses the celestial
meridian at nine o'clock in the evening during July.
Its brightest star, Antares, is decidedly red; it is the
largest known star, having a diameter more than four
hundred times the sun's diameter. Between Scorpio,
which is low in the south, and Corona, which appears
near the zenith at this season, a rather large area is
taken up by two constellations, *Serpens* and *Ophiuchus*.

Acquaintance with the conspicuous constellations is
easily gained and is profitable. Not only are these configurations interesting in themselves, but when the evening sky ceases to be a meaningless jumble of stars,
and assumes instead a familiar aspect, one looks at the
sky frequently. And he is likely to be surprised to find
that many interesting occurrences are taking place in
the heavens, which he had not noticed before.

II

THE NATURE OF A STAR

For most of the time that man has watched the stars he has accepted them simply as twinkling points of light designed to decorate the skies of the nighttime. Their grouping into striking configurations attracted attention at a very early time, and particularly their usefulness in showing the time of night and in foretelling the changing seasons.

As the science of astronomy developed, it was for many centuries confined almost entirely to those celestial bodies immediately surrounding the earth, that is to say, the sun, moon, and bright planets. The brightness of these bodies, and their motions against the background of the sphere of the stars, singled them out for special consideration. The stars in the distance remained apparently fixed and inscrutable. Yet they served as convenient landmarks for fixing the positions of the wandering bodies from time to time. On this account, primarily, the stars were mapped in early times.

After Copernicus had placed the sun in its rightful position as the central and dominating body of the planetary system, it was gradually understood that our sun is one of the stars, appearing much brighter than the others because it is much nearer. The stars then came to be regarded as distant suns, enormous, and very hot bodies, perhaps attended also by systems of planets and satellites. To this day we do not know about the truth of this surmise; for a planetary system such as ours around the nearest star would be entirely invisible with present telescopes.

What we have learned about the sun presumably applies in a general way to the stars. They are vast globes of very hot gas, having photospheres, chromospheres and prominences, and coronas. They pour forth continually into space enormous quantities of energy, from what source no one knows as yet. But even the naked eye can see that the stars are not all exact copies of our sun. There are blue stars and red stars as well as yellow ones like the sun.

Aside from a few obvious features, the telescope alone has added little to our knowledge of the nature of a star. It shows us many more stars, of course, than the naked eye can discern. But even the largest telescope is unable to magnify a single star into a disk, so that we may study the surface. It was only after the invention and application of special instruments that the phenomena of the stars themselves could be observed. Among the first to be applied, and to-day among the most effective attachments to the telescope in the study of the stars, is the spectroscope.

THE ANALYSIS OF STARLIGHT

The spectroscope, as it is employed in astronomy, is an instrument for analyzing the light of the celestial bodies. This is accomplished by means of a prism, or a number of prisms, or else a grating, which disperses the light into a colored band, or *spectrum*, having the colors of the rainbow. The colors from one end of the visible spectrum to the other are violet, blue, green, yellow, orange, and red, with gradations between.

Two small telescopes are set so that they point toward the prism. The first telescope receives the light through what would ordinarily be the eye end. Here the eyepiece is replaced by a narrow slit. When the spectroscope is attached to the telescope, this slit is placed at the focus of its objective. Having passed through the slit, the light is made parallel by the lens of the first small telescope, the collimator, whence it passes through the prism. The spectrum thus formed is observed through the second small telescope, the view telescope, or it is more often photographed. By means of reflectors placed over parts of the slit, it is possible to photograph with the spectrum of the celestial body the spectrum of a known substance, such as hydrogen or iron. This comparison spectrum is possible only with the slit spectroscope, the form just described, which, however, has the disadvantage of showing the spectrum of only one star at a time.

Another form, the objective prism spectroscope, has the merit of showing the spectra of many stars at once. It is simply a telescope with a large prism over the objective. A photograph with this arrangement shows, instead of the field of stars toward which the telescope is pointing, a short spectrum in the place of each star.

Spectrum analysis of the celestial bodies was effectively inaugurated by Fraunhofer, whom we have before mentioned as the pioneer in the making of large telescopes. In 1814, Fraunhofer examined sunlight with a spectroscope which he had made, and saw for the first time a pattern of many fine dark lines across the spectrum. He lettered the most conspicuous of the dark lines in order from the red to the violet end of the spectrum, a system which remains in use to-day. Thus two dark lines close together in the yellow region are the D lines.

Fraunhofer was the first, in 1823, to examine the spectra of the stars. He observed patterns of dark lines there also, patterns of increasing complexity with increasing redness of the star. It remained for the physicist Kirchhoff to explain the significance of these lines by his celebrated law from which we draw the following conclusions:

The spectrum of a luminous gas is ordinarily a pattern of bright lines of the various colors on a dark background; and the pattern is characteristic of the chemical element of which the gas is composed. Just as a radio station broadcasting on several different wavelengths might be identified by tuning in at those places, so each chemical element in the luminous gaseous state is identified by the selected wavelengths of light that it broadcasts.

A luminous solid, liquid, or even a gas under special conditions gives a continuous spectrum; that is to say, it emits light of all colors—white light. Now, if a cooler gas intervenes between us and such a source it will absorb from the white light precisely the wavelengths that it emits. The spectrum of the combination will be a pattern of dark lines on an otherwise continuous band of the colors. And the dark line pattern will inform us of the chemical constitution of the intervening gas. The dark line spectrum of a star signifies that selected wavelengths have been sifted out by the star's atmosphere from the white light emerging from its photosphere.

PATTERNS IN STELLAR SPECTRA

The photographic study of the spectra of the stars has been carried on for nearly fifty years at the Harvard Observatory and at its southern station at Arequipa, Peru (now moved to Mazelpoort, South Africa). In this work the objective prism has been used. Thousands of photographs of all regions of the heavens have been secured and carefully examined. As a result of this persistent investigation the spectra of more than a quarter of a million stars are known. By reference to *The Henry Draper Catalogue* one can learn the brightness and spectral class of any one of these stars. The latter term requires some explanation.

Of the many stellar spectra which have been examined, the patterns of lines, with few exceptions, can be arranged in a continuous sequence. It is almost certain that the spectrum of the next star to be studied will match somewhere along the sequence. At equal intervals the patterns are designated arbitrarily by the letters B, A, F, G, K, M. The intervals are divided into ten parts. If, for example, we examine the spectrum of a star and find that the pattern of lines is halfway between the standard patterns B and A, the spectral class of the star is B5. This convenient method of describing the spectra of the stars originated at the Harvard Observatory. It is known as the Draper Classification.

In stellar spectra of *Class B* helium lines are prominent. This gas, with which dirigibles are filled, was first detected in the sun's chromosphere, by the presence of unfamiliar lines in its spectrum. An example of a helium star is the middle star of the three in Orion's belt.

Class A spectra, those of Sirius and Vega, for example, have very prominent hydrogen lines. Hydrogen, the lightest element, is present in all classes. Thus far the stars are blue. This series of line patterns is a color gradation as well, from blue to red stars.

Class F stars, such as the polestar and the great Canopus in the southern hemisphere, are yellowish. In their spectra the hydrogen lines are somewhat less conspicuous, while lines of the metals, calcium, iron, and others, are appearing in great numbers.

The sun is typical of a *Class G* star. It is a yellow star, its spectrum is crossed by thousands of metallic lines. In *Class K*, to which the orange star Arcturus belongs, metallic lines are still more prominent. Toward the end of this class, and in the following *Class M* of red stars such as Betelgeuse, in Orion, and Antares, in Scorpio, bands or flutings are to be seen in the spectra, as well as many lines.

Such is the principal part of the spectral sequence. Four other classes are recognized, which contain all together not more than one per cent of the stars. It was formerly imagined that this sequence, from blue to red stars, represents the life history of a star. Thus the blue stars are young, the yellow stars like the sun are middle aged, while the red stars are destined to grow redder and dimmer as time goes on, and finally to vanish from sight. A later theory held that one group of red stars represents extreme youth. As the star ages, it becomes yellow, then blue, and reverts finally to red again in its old age. Still other theories of stellar evolution have appeared. For the present, we do not know how the stars came to be, or how, having appeared, they have grown.

TEMPERATURES OF THE STARS

A piece of metal is at a higher temperature when it is blue hot than when it is red hot. Similarly, we may suppose that the atmosphere of a blue star has a higher temperature than that of a red star. Appropriate investigations show that our supposition is correct, that the spectral sequence represents a gradation of diminishing temperatures. Measurements of stellar spectra not only establish this fact, but also give values of the temperature for stars of the different spectral classes. In recent years it has been possible, in addition, to measure the heating effect produced by the stars.

In the chapter on the sun it was pointed out that the sun's temperature can be determined by placing a pan of water in the sunshine, observing the rise in temperature of the water, and making certain calculations. Evidently this crude procedure would not be satisfactory for the stars. Pettit and Nicholson accomplish the same result in a different way. With the 100-inch telescope on Mount Wilson they focus the light of a star on a tiny thermocouple, and observe the heating effect by the deflection of a galvanometer. In this way they can measure the heat produced by a star hundreds of times too faint to be visible to the naked eye, and therefore the temperature of the star. They have employed the same method to determine the temperatures of the planets, and of different parts of the moon's surface.

Temperatures immediately above the photosphere of the blue stars range from ten to twenty thousand degrees Centigrade, and perhaps higher. Surface temperatures of the yellow stars are around six thousand degrees Centigrade, and of the reddest stars around two thousand degrees. Even the coolest stars are still very hot.

Below the photosphere the star's temperature rises enormously with increasing depth, perhaps to many millions of degrees at the center. The conclusions of different authorities are for the present far from agreement as to conditions in the interiors of the stars. Whence comes the energy that keeps the stars shining, and where does all the starlight go are other problems of the greatest interest which require further investigation.

GIANT AND DWARF STARS

The stars vary enormously in actual brightness, or *luminosity*. If we could place them along with the sun in a row all at the same distance, we should then discover that they range from a ten thousandth to more than ten thousand times the sun's brightness. In practice, astronomers observe how bright they would appear if they were viewed from some standard distance. How these distances are determined will be learned in the following chapter.

On a sheet of paper ruled in squares let us place a dot in the appropriate place for each star whose luminosity and spectral class are known. A "spectrum-

luminosity diagram" of this sort is shown in Figure
43. The vertical lines represent the different spectral

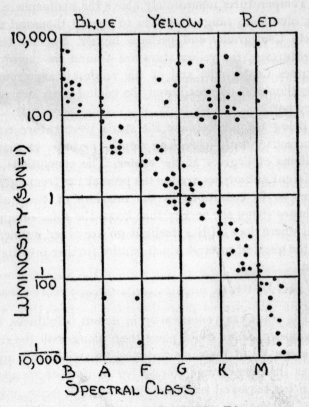

FIG. 43. *Spectrum-Luminosity Diagram*

classes, from the blue to the red stars, toward the right.
The horizontal lines represent different degrees of
actual brightness in terms of the sun's brightness, increasing upward. The dot for the sun, class G0, is in
the middle of the diagram.

The dots for the majority of the stars, including the sun, lie near the diagonal, from upper left to lower right. This is the *main sequence*. Along this diagonal toward the right the stars become cooler, therefore redder and fainter. The steepness of the slope suggests that they become smaller also.

Above the main sequence, two groups of stars are represented by the dots. They are the *giant stars* which average around a hundred times the sun's luminosity, and the *supergiants* which are thousands of times brighter than the sun. Consider the stars of a specified class, say the red class M stars. Since they are of the same color, their surface temperatures are the same, and their surface brightness is the same per square yard. A square yard of the surface of any one of these stars is equal in brightness to a square yard of any other. That the giants and supergiants are many times brighter than corresponding stars of the main sequence signifies that their surfaces contain many more square yards; they are so much brighter because they are enormously larger.

One other group of dots is noticed in the diagram, a small group standing apart in the lower left corner. They are the *white dwarf stars*, of which the faint companion of Sirius is the best known. A thousand times or more fainter than the white stars generally, they must be correspondingly smaller. It is true that the white dwarfs are no fainter than the red stars of the main sequence, but they must be smaller than these also; for each square yard of a white star is brighter than that of a red star. The white dwarfs are the smallest stars known.

DIMENSIONS OF THE STARS

Stars are "weighed" in much the same way that planets are weighed, namely, by the strength of their attractions for neighboring bodies. We have already noticed that it is difficult to determine precisely the mass of a solitary planet such as Mercury, which has no satellite. But the problem is a simple one if the planet is attended by satellites. It is even more difficult to determine the mass of a single star. The spaces separating the stars are so enormous that the gravitational effect of one star on another cannot be observed.

Fortunately for the accomplishment of the weighing, the telescope reveals thousands of pairs of stars—binaries, many of them certainly in mutual revolution. The spectroscope shows many closer pairs. At a specified distance apart the period of revolution is shorter, the larger the combined mass of the pair. When the mean separation and the period of revolution can be determined, the calculation of the combined mass is easily performed. In addition, it is sometimes possible to determine the masses of individual stars of the binary systems.

The striking conclusion from such studies of double stars is that the masses of the stars are fairly uniform. Almost all range from one fifth to five times the sun's mass. These building blocks of which the universe is constructed contain about the same amount of material, and of them our sun is a fair average. It is by no means a second-rate star, as some apologists would have us believe. We may well take a reasonable amount of pride in it.

Our examination of Figure 43 has already given considerable information as to the sizes of different classes of stars. It would seem that the stars of the main sequence which are bluer than the sun must be somewhat larger than the sun; those which are redder must be somewhat smaller. The white dwarfs are evidently much smaller. Giant stars are much larger, while the red supergiants are largest of all. Calculations based on the data that we find in the diagram have led to these conclusions, and have given fairly trustworthy values of the diameters of individual stars. Direct measurement of the size of a star, as one might measure the diameter of the moon or a planet, is impossible, because no star appears as a true disk even in the largest telescope. If we keep this in mind, we cannot fail to be impressed by the ingenuity which astronomers have exercised in getting so much information out of those points of light that we call stars.

In recent years, beginning in 1920, Michelson's adaptation of the interferometer for the measurement of stellar diameters has been employed at Mount Wilson, first in connection with the 100-inch reflector, and later as a separate instrument fifty feet wide. The procedure is a little complicated. It is sufficient to say that the interferometer measures the diameters of some of the stars very satisfactorily. The largest star so far measured is Antares, whose diameter is four hundred million miles. Betelgeuse, the first to be measured, is about half as large. These and other red supergiants are enormous, as the calculations require.

Since the masses of the stars are fairly uniform, and since the amount of space that this material occupies varies greatly, the densities of the stars must differ enormously. In the red supergiants the material is spread out extremely thin. Antares, for example, is only one three-thousandth as dense as the air around us.

At the other extreme, the white dwarfs seem to be compressed to a degree that only a few years ago would have been considered quite impossible. In size they resemble the planets. In amount of material they are comparable with the sun. The faint companion of Sirius averages thirty thousand times denser than water. The suggestion is made that the atoms within the star have been almost completely shattered at the very high temperatures prevailing there, permitting a high compression of matter that is unobtainable on the earth.

Despite this evidence, which seems difficult to deny, not all astronomers and physicists are agreed that it must be accepted. Indeed, everyone might still be incredulous that the companion of Sirius can possibly be thirty thousand times denser than water—in other words, that an ordinary tumblerful of material from this star can weigh as much as seven or eight tons, if it were not supported by independent evidence. In accordance with the theory of relativity the spectrum of a very dense star should have its lines strongly displaced toward the red end. Such a displacement in the spectrum of the companion of Sirius has been observed at Mount Wilson, and again at the Lick Observatory.

PULSATING STARS

The majority of the stars shine with a constant light. When we consider the vast amount of energy streaming away from the photosphere of a star, we are impressed by the efficient operations within the star that can deliver energy to the photosphere in precisely the required amount, second after second, century after century. In many stars, however, the output of radiation is not constant. Such stars are known as variable stars. We reserve for a later description those stars which are variable in light owing to eclipses.

Mira, a red star in Cetus, was the first variable star to be recognized, as early as 1596. At times it is visible only with the telescope as a star of the ninth magnitude. On other occasions it is more than a hundred times brighter, appearing as a fairly bright star to the naked eye. The fluctuations are completed in cycles of about eleven months. Mira is an example of the numerous class of *long-period variables*. They are red giant stars and supergiant stars. Many other great red stars, such as Betelgeuse, vary in an entirely irregular way within narrower limits of brightness. A few groups of stars vary in light in a partially predictable fashion.

Cepheid variable stars are at present the most widely discussed; and certainly they have the greatest value, as the following chapter shows. Named after Delta Cephei, one of the first examples of this kind of variation to be recognized, typical Cepheids are yellow supergiants. Their fluctuations recur with great regularity both in time and in manner of variation, in periods most generally around a week, although they range all the way from one to fifty days. These stars vary not only in quantity of light, but in quality as well. At their brightest they are bluer by something like a whole spectral class than at minimum light.

Nearly half of the Cepheids are not of the kind just described as typical. While they have a number of characteristics in common with the others, they exhibit important differences from them. By virtue of their frequent occurrence in the great globular clusters, they are known as *cluster type Cepheids*. They are blue stars, and the periods of their fluctuations are around half a day. Not one is bright enough to be visible to the naked eye.

It is generally supposed that the variability in the light of the Cepheids, and perhaps of all other true variable stars as well, is caused by the pulsations of these stars. In its simplest form, which may be too simple, the theory holds that the variable star is rhythmically expanding and contracting. An overproduction of heat in the interior makes the star brighter and bluer. It expands, thereby becoming cooler, and thus fainter and redder. This adjustment is overdone; the star is cooled too much for stability, so that it contracts again. And this pulsation, once started, continues for a very long time. An apparent difficulty with the simple theory, not at once easy to justify, is the observed fact that the Cepheid is brightest not when it is most compressed, but a quarter of the period later, when it is expanding most vigorously. Evidently the problem of stellar variability is closely associated with the whole question of the nature of a star.

TEMPORARY STARS

"New stars" are the most amazing of the stars, and indeed among the most surprising of all the spectacles that the heavens display. Called *novæ*, they are not new stars in fact, but faint stars apparently as constant as the majority, which for reasons unknown to us suddenly explode. In a few hours they rise from obscurity to enormously greater brilliancy. At the height of their temporary splendor they sometimes rival the brightest stars, and, more rarely, the brightest planets. More gradually they then subside to comparative obscurity.

The finest nova on record appeared in 1572, in the constellation Cassiopeia. It is often referred to as "Tycho's star," because that celebrated astronomer observed it, although he was not the first to see it. It rose suddenly to a grandeur equal to that of Venus, and thereafter faded, until about six months later it disappeared from view. "Kepler's star" in Ophiuchus was superior to Jupiter. It burst upon the celestial scene in 1604 and remained visible to the naked eye fully a year and a half. There were then no telescopes to watch it further.

Thus far in the present century, four very bright novæ have appeared. Nova Persei, in 1901, became a little brighter than Capella. Nova Aquilæ, in 1918, the brightest in more than three centuries, exceeded every star except Sirius. In two or three days it increased in brightness nearly fifty thousand times. Nova Cygni, in 1920, became nearly as bright as Deneb, at the top of the Northern Cross. Nova Pictoris, in 1925, appeared at its brightest as a star of the first magnitude.

These are exceptionally bright novæ. Many at their maxima are not visible to the naked eye. Some of these are picked up on the photographs. Doubtless many rise and fade unobserved by anyone. It is estimated that as many as twenty temporary stars bright enough to be seen with a small telescope burst forth yearly among the stars around us, while multitudes appear in the external galaxies.

Temporary stars are not so rare, after all. Throughout the long lives of the stars it may well be that every star at some time in its career explodes in this remarkable way. And considerable interest is added by the thought that our own sun may some day explode likewise. Such an event would undoubtedly constitute a major catastrophe for all life on the earth. We wonder by what tangle in the ordinarily smooth operations of the stars these explosions can come about. Although astronomers, by means of the telescope, spectroscope, and photographic plate, have assembled much information concerning the upheaval, they have not yet located the cause. When this becomes known, we shall be much farther advanced in our understanding of the nature of a star.

Having now examined various characteristics of the stars, as they are known to us, we may ask and briefly answer in summary the question implied by the heading of this chapter. What is a star? The poet who wrote, "Twinkle, twinkle, little star, how I wonder what you are," was doubtless content to wonder. The astronomer has been wondering, and also persistently endeavoring to find out. That, of course, is his business. How well he has succeeded in the very short interval in which it has been possible to inquire effectively, we have seen.

The stars are the power houses of the universe, and

the building blocks with which nature has erected intricate and colossal structures. They are balls of intensely hot gas. The quantity of gas they contain does not vary very much from star to star. In size, however, they vary enormously; their diameters range from hundreds of millions of miles among the red supergiants to mere tens of thousands of miles among the white dwarfs. The former average thousands of times lighter than air; the latter, tens of thousands of times heavier than water. At their centers the density becomes very great, at least, and the temperature amazingly high. Some stars vary in light, suggesting pulsations. Some explode. Such are the stars.

III

THE DISTANCES OF THE STARS

THE principles on which distances in the heavens are measured were explained in the chapter concerning the scale of the solar system. For distances of the moon, the planets, and other near-by objects we use as the base line for measurement the radius of the earth, or in practice, the line joining two points of observation on its surface. But this is entirely too short to serve for measuring a distance so great as that even of the nearest star. For this purpose we take as the base line the radius of the earth's orbit, or in practice the line joining two positions of the earth near opposite extremities of its orbit. Even with this much greater separation of the two points of observation, the displacements of the stars are extremely small.

Let the little circle on the left in Figure 44 represent the earth's orbit. Let S be one of the nearer stars, whose distance we wish to measure. Let the dotted lines show the practically invariable direction of a remote star, T. When the earth is at one side of its orbit, at P, we measure the angle, SPT, between the two stars. When the earth is at the opposite side, we measure the corresponding angle, SQT. The difference, PSQ, between these two angles, divided by two, is the *parallax* of the star. Strictly, it is the relative parallax that is observed. For the distant star may be displaced slightly. If this can be determined and allowed for, the final result is the absolute parallax which is required.

In practice, it is not sufficient to observe the star's direction on only two occasions. While the stars might seem to be fixed, they are really in rapid motion, so that they are steadily changing their directions. This *proper motion* is especially conspicuous with the telescope for the nearer stars. We are therefore uncertain after two observations at an interval of six months as to how much of the observed displacement of our star

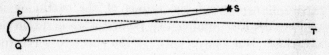

Fig. 44.   *Measurement of the Parallax of a Star*

is owing to its own motion, and how much is the parallax effect of our change of position. In order to disentangle the two, the observations must be continued over two or three years.

Modern parallax determinations are photographic. Plates are exposed at the focus of a long telescope which is directed to the region containing the star to be investigated. At intervals of about six months thereafter, other plates are taken of the same region. The positions of the star on these plates are measured with the greatest care with reference to fainter and presumably more remote stars around it; comparison stars, they are called. The work is very exacting; for the displacement of the nearest star is only one and a half seconds of arc. This is the angle subtended by an object an inch in diameter viewed at a distance of more than two miles. For the majority of the stars so measured the displacement is very much smaller.

When the amount of the parallax has been determined, the calculation of the star's distance is easily performed; and there is a choice of ways of expressing the result. To obtain the distance in astronomical units, the mean distance of the earth from the sun, divide the number 206,265 by the parallax. Thus the parallax of Alpha Centauri, long supposed to be the nearest star, is 0″.76. It is therefore about 270,000 times more remote than the sun, or twenty-five million million miles. These numbers are inconveniently large. Astronomers prefer to express stellar distances in larger units, either the parsec or the light-year.

The *parsec* is the distance at which the parallax would be one second of arc. No star is in fact as close as this. To obtain the distance in parsecs, divide the number one by the parallax. The distance of Alpha Centauri is therefore 1.3 parsecs.

The *light-year* is the distance traversed by light in a year. In miles, it is 186,284, the speed of light in one second, multiplied by the number of seconds in a year, about 31.6 million, or nearly six million million miles. A parsec equals about three and a quarter light-years. The distance of Alpha Centauri is 4.3 light-years.

The nearest star, Proxima, is three per cent nearer than Alpha Centauri, or about four and a sixth light-years from the sun. It is a telescopic star of the tenth magnitude, located in the sky a little more than two degrees from Alpha, and probably physically associated with this bright star, happening to be on the side

ing in toward the opposite point in the heavens. Herschel located the former point, the *solar apex* in the constellation Hercules, not far from the bright star Vega, in Lyra; and near this location subsequent investigations have placed it also.

This apparent backward movement of the stars informs us in what direction the sun is taking us, but not how fast we are going. It remained for the spectroscope to supply this information. We have already learned that the spectrum of a star is a band of rainbow colors crossed, in general, by dark lines. In accordance with a principle stated by Doppler, nearly a century ago, and more specifically set forth by Fizeau, somewhat later, the spectral lines tell us how the star is moving in the line of sight. If the star is relatively approaching, the lines in its spectrum are displaced toward the violet end. If it is receding, the lines are displaced toward the red. And the amount of the displacement increases with the speed.

Evidently, the stars in the region of the heavens toward which the solar system is moving will collectively seem to be approaching with the greatest speed. Those in the opposite part of the sky will seem to be withdrawing from us with the greatest speed. As the result of a thirty years' study of stellar spectra in all parts of the sky, now completed by the astronomers of the Lick Observatory, we have further information on the direction of the solar motion and the determination of its speed.

With respect to the stars around us, the solar system is moving toward a point in the heavens closely marked by the star Omicron Herculis, and at the rate of 12.3

miles a second. Relative to these stars, the earth is then moving in a helix, revolving around the sun and sharing in the sun's forward motion meanwhile.

In its motion along with the sun the earth takes us twice the distance across its orbit. All the stars are shifted backward twice the amount of their greatest displacement caused by the earth's revolution around the sun. In a century it is two hundred times as great. Here is a base line, the line of the sun's way toward Hercules, that seems at first to fulfill all our requirements for measurements of stellar distances. The parallactic motion depends on the star's distance, and by its amount informs us how great the distance is. Unfortunately, however, for the successful measurement of distances in this way, it is not possible ordinarily to determine what part of the observed displacement is parallactic, and what part is owing to the motion of the star itself. The method does not serve for individual stars.

ABSOLUTE MAGNITUDES OF THE STARS

The stars, as we observe them, differ greatly in brightness. If the stars were all of the same actual brightness—if they should prove to be equally bright viewed from the same distance, the problem of celestial distances would be a simple one. Consider, on this assumption, two stars of different apparent brightness. The fainter star would be the more remote; and since the observed brightness of a point of light varies inversely as the square of the distance, we could easily determine how much the distance of the fainter star exceeds that of the brighter. But we know that the stars are not equally luminous. Our problem then resolves itself into the following question: Can we by any means determine the absolute brightness of a star whose distance is unknown? If so, we can easily calculate the distance, by comparing the absolute with the observed brightness. Recent discoveries have made this procedure possible. First let us understand the meaning of the terms "apparent magnitude" and "absolute magnitude."

Ancient astronomers, some two thousand years ago, divided the lucid stars into six classes, or *magnitudes*, in order of diminishing brightness. About twenty of the brightest stars comprised the first magnitude. Conspicuous stars not among the very brightest, including the polestar and all but one of the stars of the Great Dipper, were designated as stars of the second magnitude. And so on, to the sixth magnitude, which was reserved for stars barely visible to the naked eye. These are *apparent magnitudes*, indicating observed brightness.

After the invention of the telescope, the scheme of magnitudes was extended to include the fainter stars which it brings into view. Stars as faint as the twenty-first magnitude can be observed with the 100-inch telescope. The plan was given precision, also, by the rule that the ratio of brightness between two stars differing by exactly one magnitude is 2.512. Thus a star of the first magnitude is two and a half times brighter than one of the second magnitude. Some revision was necessary among the very brightest stars which show a considerable range of brightness. Vega, for example, is of about magnitude zero, and Sirius, brightest of the stars, is of magnitude —1.6. The sun's apparent magnitude is —26.7.

These are visual apparent magnitudes, observed directly with the eye or the eye at the telescope. Of two stars of different colors, whose visual magnitudes are the same, the redder will appear the fainter on the ordinary photographic plate. Photographic magnitudes differ from visual, particularly for the red stars. There are other magnitude systems, depending on the particular apparatus employed.

Absolute magnitude is the magnitude which a star would have if its distance were exactly ten parsecs—the distance at which its parallax would be one tenth of a second of arc. If the star's distance is known, it is easy to calculate from its observed magnitude the value of its absolute magnitude. Thus the absolute visual magnitude of Antares is —4.0, of Sirius +1.3, of the sun +4.8. At the standard distance of ten parsecs, Antares would rival the planet Venus near greatest brilliancy; Sirius would be a star of the first magnitude; the sun would appear as a faint star.

A simple calculation shows that our sun would become invisible to the naked eye if its distance were increased to twenty parsecs, about the distance of the first magnitude star Aldebaran. At the distance of 6,300 parsecs, or 20,000 light-years, a little more than halfway to the globular cluster in Hercules, the sun would become invisible with the largest telescope.

The modern method of measuring the distances of celestial bodies too remote to be within the very limited reach of direct parallax observations is to determine their absolute magnitudes. Two ways will be mentioned by which the absolute magnitudes of stars of hitherto unknown distances are revealed to us. The first is by special studies of the spectra of stars; the second is by observations of Cepheid variable stars.

DISTANCES WITH THE SPECTROSCOPE

Ordinarily, we do not think of the spectroscope as an instrument for measuring distances. Its service is primarily the analysis of light. But in 1914, astronomers at the Mount Wilson Observatory discovered a way to find the absolute magnitude of a star by examining certain lines in its spectrum. In the meantime, "spectroscopic parallaxes" of thousands of stars have been evaluated at this and other observatories.

In the description of the spectral sequence, in the preceding chapter, it was pointed out that this sequence, from blue to red stars, is produced by the diminishing surface temperatures. Just as iron boils at a higher temperature than water, so the different chemical elements in the star's atmosphere absorb their characteristic patterns of lines most effectively at different temperatures. Thus the patterns change as we proceed along the spectral sequence. All stars of the same spectral class have approximately the same surface temperature and show approximately the same pattern of lines in their spectra.

There is another factor we have so far neglected, namely, pressure. Just as water boils at a lower temperature when the pressure is reduced, as on a mountain, so a chemical element can show its spectrum lines equally well at a lower temperature, if the pressure is less. Now the pressures at the surfaces of stars of a specified spectral class, say M0, are reduced as we proceed upward in the diagram of Figure 43 to the larger stars. The temperature diminishes to maintain the same pattern of lines. Thus the rarer red giants are somewhat cooler than the denser red stars of the main sequence.

This compromise between temperature and pressure does not affect equally all the chemical elements. While the pattern is maintained approximately, a few lines become progressively stronger, and a few others grow fainter with increasing absolute brightness. This is the relation on which the method depends. By measuring the intensities of these sensitive lines in the spectrum of a star, it is possible to say what the absolute magnitude of the star must be, and therefore to establish the distance of the star.

DISTANCES OF THE CEPHEIDS

Cepheids, as we have seen, are stars which vary regularly in light in cycles ranging from a few hours to several weeks. They fall into two classes: cluster type Cepheids having periods around half a day, and typical Cepheids whose periods are most frequently around a week. The former are blue stars; the latter are yellow supergiants. Both vary through a range of about a magnitude, and in color as well as in brightness. It is believed that they are pulsating stars. But their value in the present connection is quite apart from any theory concerning the cause of their variation. By virtue of a relation clearly established between the period of the fluctuation and the absolute magnitude, Cepheids have assumed a place of the greatest importance in the exploration of the universe.

This relation was first noticed in 1912, by Miss Leavitt at the Harvard Observatory. In the course of a study of Cepheid variable stars in the Small Magellanic Cloud, a remote assemblage to be described in a later chapter, she observed that the period of the fluctuation increases in a simple way with the apparent magnitude of the star. Since the differences in distance between the stars of the Cloud are small in comparison with the great distance of the whole group, the apparent magnitudes of these stars have nearly the same relation as their absolute magnitudes. A few years later, Shapley set forth the more general aspects of this connection. He prepared a curve showing how the period increases with the median absolute magnitude; that is to say, the average between the brightest and faintest magnitudes of the star.

If the period of the light variation is half a day, the median absolute photographic magnitude is 0.0; if it is one day, the magnitude is —0.3; ten days, magnitude —1.9; a hundred days, magnitude —4.6. These are a few readings from the curve which applies to Cepheid variables everywhere, no matter how remote. The procedure is simple. First, find a Cepheid, a variable star whose fluctuations exhibit the characteristics we have noticed. Observe it from night to night until the period of the fluctuation is determined. Read from the curve the corresponding absolute magnitude. Having derived the median apparent magnitude from the observations, calculate the distance.

The first of the directions is to find the Cepheid. But these variable stars are rare. Perhaps not more than one star in a million is a typical Cepheid, to which the curve applies. Fortunately, the yellow Cepheids are supergiants, among the brightest stars absolutely. We can see them a long way off, certainly farther away even than a million light years. They appear in various parts of our Milky Way system, in the globular clusters that hover around its outskirts, and in the galaxies which lie beyond the Milky Way. Wherever a Cepheid is discerned, its distance can be determined, and therefore the distance of the assemblage that contains it.

Cluster type Cepheids are equally valuable for finding distances. For their shorter periods, Shapley's curve becomes horizontal at absolute magnitude zero. This is the value for all such variable stars. It is an even simpler matter to determine their distances. By means of Cepheids chiefly, and by other devices for finding absolute magnitudes, astronomers are to-day surveying the stellar system around us and the remote systems beyond with a precision that only a few years ago would have seemed quite impossible.

IV
STELLAR SYSTEMS

In the choice of companions for their long journeys through space, stars resemble people. Some plod along alone, in straight lines with unvarying speeds, practically uninfluenced by their fellows. Others travel in pairs, either side by side, or else mutually revolving in unending dance. These are the *binary stars*. Others are to be found in small groups, the *multiple stars;* still others in crowds, the *star clusters*. But whether solitary or companionable, they are included in larger divisions of stellar society, the *star clouds*, or *galaxies*. Gregariousness is a pronounced characteristic of celestial bodies. Let us examine the different ways in which the stars are assembled in systems.

VISUAL BINARY STARS

Mizar, the second from the end in the handle of the Great Dipper, is a famous double star. Even a small telescope resolves it into two stars of unequal brightness. This fact was recorded as early as 1650. Subsequently, other stars, apparently single to the naked eye, proved to be double when they were viewed with the telescope. But their significance was not understood at the time, and little attention was given them. Indeed, it could readily be imagined that among the multitude of stars two would often have so nearly the same direction, though one might be far behind the other, that they would appear as one. A little calculation shows, however, that such accidental or *optical double stars* must be far less numerous than the doubles that are observed. It seems probable, therefore, that they are actually close together; and the less the angular separation of the pairs, the greater the probability of their physical association. Such double stars as they are revealed by the telescope are known as *visual double stars*.

The majority of the visual binaries are traveling side by side, with no evidence of mutual revolution. Many others are revolving systems, like the earth and the sun, though their separations and periods are greater. Delta Equulei is remarkable for its short period of less than six years; the separation of the pair is less than Jupiter's distance from the sun. Other examples of revolving systems are Alpha Centauri, having a period of nearly eighty years and an average separation somewhat greater than the distance of Uranus from the sun, and Castor whose two stars revolve in the period of about three hundred years, with a mean separation twice Pluto's distance from the sun. Castor was, in fact, the first double system known to be in revolution. William Herschel, in 1803, noticed that the line joining the two stars had certainly changed direction since Bradley had recorded it nearly a century before him. This discovery was important. Up to this time, astronomers, including Herschel himself, had regarded telescopic double stars as optical doubles simply. It became evident then that at least some of them are actually physical systems. Then began the discovery and study of visual binaries which have continued vigorously to the present time, and in recent years have been extended to the region around the south celestial pole which was invisible to most of the earlier investigators.

Aitken, at the Lick Observatory, is generally regarded as the greatest living authority on visual binary stars. More than thirty years ago he undertook the examination of every star brighter than the ninth magnitude within convenient reach of his telescope. This program, on which he worked single-handed for the greater part of the time, was completed in 1915. It resulted in the discovery of 4,300 visual binaries. Aitken's recently published catalogue of known visual binaries within 120° of the north celestial pole contains more than seventeen thousand entries. His conclusion that one star in eighteen brighter than the ninth magnitude is a binary of this sort applies to the southern skies also, as the more recent discoveries in these regions are showing.

Observations of these binary stars are usually made visually, with the eye at the telescope. In place of the simple eyepiece, the micrometer is employed. This instrument contains a spider thread which can be moved parallel to itself across the field of view, and also rotated, both motions being measured by accurate scales. The observation consists in measuring with the micrometer the angular separation of the two stars and the direction of the fainter, *companion* star with respect to the brighter one. When the measures have been continued until the companion has performed a complete revolution, or enough of its circuit to show clearly what the remainder will be, the calculation of the orbit can proceed. The resulting elements of the relative orbit are the seven specifications, such as the size, eccentricity, and inclination, which completely define it. Usually, it is impossible to determine from the data which side of the orbit is toward us. These orbits are inclined at various angles to the plane of the sky. In general, they are much more flattened ellipses than are the planetary orbits.

The Dog Stars, Sirius and Procyon, are especially noteworthy examples of visual binaries. Among the nearest stars, at distances of 8.8 and 10.4 light-years respectively, they have conspicuous motions among the stars. About a century ago, it was definitely established that these two bright stars are not pursuing straight courses as they should if they were single stars. Instead, their paths are wavy, showing that they are both attended by fainter companions with which they revolve as they move forward. As in the case of Neptune, and perhaps also of the recently discovered planet Pluto, these faint companions of the Dog Stars were known to exist before anyone had seen them. The companion of Sirius was first discerned with the telescope in 1862; that of Procyon remained unseen until 1896.

SPECTROSCOPIC BINARIES

Just as many stars which appear single to the naked eye are resolved by the telescope into pairs, so there are many stars apparently single in the largest telescopes whose duplicity is revealed by the spectroscope. Unless the orbit of the revolving star is presented flatwise to the earth, the star alternately approaches and recedes from us. As it approaches, the lines of its spectrum are displaced toward the violet end; as it recedes, the lines are displaced toward the red. This is the well known Doppler effect. Thus the regular oscillation of the lines in the spectrum of a star, if it cannot be assigned to the earth's revolution, stamps it as one member of a *spectroscopic binary;* and the period of the oscillation is that of revolution of the binary. If the companion star is of comparable brightness, its lines appear also. If the two stars are of the same spectral class, the two similar patterns shift back and forth in opposite phase, so that the lines are sometimes double and at other times single, when they are superposed.

Mizar, in the Great Dipper, was the first spectroscopic binary to be recognized. Curiously enough, this star was also the first visual binary to be recorded. In 1889, it was noticed at the Harvard Observatory that the lines in the spectrum of the brighter star of the visual pair were double on some of the photographs and single on others. These two stars cannot be separated with the telescope. They are mutually revolving in a period of twenty days and a half. Their average distance apart is somewhat greater than the distance of Uranus from the sun.

In the meantime, more than a thousand spectroscopic binaries have been discovered, including some of the brightest stars, such as Capella, Spica, and Castor. Capella consists of two yellow stars of nearly equal brightness which revolve in a period of 102 days. The two blue stars which form the system of Spica are closer together. Revolving at the rates of 80 and 130 miles a second, they complete the circuit in four days. Each of the pair into which Castor is divided by the telescope is a spectroscopic binary, making four stars in all where the naked eye sees only one. Great variety is exhibited by such doubles. Some revolve almost in contact, in periods of a few hours. Others require months for a single revolution, and are so far apart that they are likely to be separated as visual binaries by larger telescopes of the future.

Three lines in the spectra of many of these revolving stars do not oscillate with the others. They are Fraunhofer lines H and K of calcium, in the violet, and the double D line of sodium in the yellow. It is believed that these dark lines are absorbed while the starlight is on its way to the earth, by a very tenuous gaseous medium in space.

Binary stars are numerous. Probably one star in every four is either double or multiple. Some astronomers have held the opinion that single stars, such as our sun, may even be in the minority. A complete account of the nature of the stars might be expected to inform us why so many are double. The fission theory of their formation has received much attention. It pictures a single star breaking in two by virtue of its rapid rotation. Jeans has imagined that the pulsations of the Cepheid variable stars might originate in the process of fission. Once separated, the two stars form a close spectroscopic binary system. By action of their mutual tides, the separations and periods of revolution could increase somewhat, but it is scarcely probable that this could continue until the stars draw apart to the wider dimensions of a visual system.

Aside from these considerations the chief importance of binary systems is in the determinations of the masses of the stars. For visual binaries the calculation is especially simple. The cube of the mean separation of the two stars, in seconds of arc, divided by the product of the cube of the parallax, in seconds, and the square of period, in years, gives the sum of the masses of the two stars. The masses are expressed in terms of the sun's mass. As we have already noticed, the masses of individual stars are not greatly different from the sun's mass. Indeed, if we put the sum of the masses equal to two in the rule just given, with a correction depending on the kinds of stars in the pair, we calculate the parallax of the binary—the dynamical parallax, it is called—which gives the distance with considerable accuracy.

ECLIPSING BINARIES

Spectroscopic binaries whose orbits are nearly edgewise, or whose stars have very small separation, are also eclipsing binaries, or eclipsing variable stars. First discovered of this numerous class, Algol, the winking "Demon Star" in Perseus, is also the most famous. Its protracted winks occur regularly at intervals of about 2 days 21 hours. For nearly two and a half days Algol remains so nearly constant in brightness that only the most accurate observations can detect any change. In the following five hours it is gradually dimmed to one third its normal brightness. In five hours more it has risen to normal again.

During the ten hours of conspicuously varying light, the bright star is being partially eclipsed by its fainter companion. We know that the eclipse is partial because the recovery of light immediately follows the decline. If it were total, the light would remain constant at its minimum during the course of the total eclipse. If the eclipse were annular, that is to say, if the star in front were completely projected on the disk of the eclipsed star without entirely hiding it, there would be a constant minimum, but the decline and recovery would be somewhat different in character. Other eclipsing binaries furnish examples of total and annular eclipses.

In the intervals between the principal eclipses the light is not constant. In some cases the variations are conspicuous, especially near the halfway point when the fainter star is being eclipsed by the brighter one. Variations outside the eclipses are produced especially by the departures of the stars from spherical form. In addition to flattening at the poles caused by the rotation of the stars, they are elongated by tides one in the direction of the other.

By accurate measurements of the light of an eclipsing binary during the full course of its variation, and especially when the spectra of the two stars has been observed also, it is possible to obtain almost complete information about the two stars and their orbits. The sizes and forms of the stars which come out in the calculations are data of the greatest value. Among the lucid stars, in addition to Algol, which are eclipsing binaries and whose variations are great enough to be easily observed are Beta Lyræ, Lambda Tauri, u Herculis, and Delta Libræ.

Eclipsing systems are special cases of spectroscopic

binaries. Their orbits are nearly edgewise to the earth. Observed from another part of the stellar system, these stars would be invariable in light, while other close binaries whose light is constant for us would wink periodically as the result of mutual eclipse.

CLUSTERS OF STARS

Star clusters are not temporary congestions in the celestial traffic. They are companies of stars traveling together through space in a perfectly orderly way. They are of two kinds; the open clusters, sometimes called galactic clusters because they are concentrated in the Milky Way, and globular clusters.

In some of the nearer open clusters the brightest stars are plainly visible to the naked eye. This is true of the Pleiades, or "Seven Sisters." Seven lucid stars form a short-handled dipper in the evening skies of the fall and winter. A keen eye may discern nine or ten stars in the cluster, while the telescope shows many more. South of the Pleiades there is another conspicuous open cluster, the Hyades, in the same constellation Taurus. They form a V-shaped group marking the head of the celestial Bull, and containing the bright reddish star Aldebaran, although this star does not belong to the cluster proper.

The members of an open cluster have a common motion through space. But some of them that are near enough to make their motions specially noticeable have been known as moving clusters. Of these the Hyades cluster is a fine example. The stars of this V-shaped group, with the exception of Aldebaran, and other stars in the neighborhood are moving together toward the east. Their paths do not appear exactly parallel; they are converging like the rails of a track in the distance, showing that the cluster is receding also. Nearly a million years ago the cluster passed us at the distance of 65 light-years. Now it is twice as far away. In less than a hundred million years the cluster will have shrunk in the distance to a faint telescopic object not far from the direction of the red star Betelgeuse, in Orion.

We are at present within such a moving cluster, though our sun is not a member. Part of this cluster appears in the northern sky, forming the Great Dipper, with the exceptions of the star at the end of the handle, and the upper star of the two Pointers in the bowl, which are not members. Sirius, far to the south, and other bright stars in widely different parts of the sky are members. Eventually they will leave us behind and will assume at a greater distance the ordinary appearance of an open star cluster.

Some of the open clusters appear as foggy patches to the naked eye. The Praesepe cluster, known also as the "Beehive," is a well known example. A little way west of the sickle of Leo, Praesepe belongs to the zodiacal constellation Cancer. Even a field glass resolves this faintly luminous spot into a coarse cluster of stars. Another cloudy spot lies directly in the Milky Way, in the constellation Perseus and not far from Cassiopeia's Chair. A small telescope shows two clusters here, known familiarly as the double cluster in Perseus. As we sweep along the Milky Way with the telescope, we encounter other fine open clusters. Some of the nearest clusters, as might be expected, are far outside this luminous band of the sky. The Coma Berenices cluster, between Leo and Boötes, is near the north pole of the Milky Way.

Cepheid variable stars and cluster type variables, which are very valuable aids in measuring distances, are not found in open clusters. In fact, no variable star of any kind has been discovered in any of these clusters. Astronomers have devised other ways, however, of determining their distances. Trumpler, at the Lick Observatory, has recently measured the distances and sizes of more than a hundred. Curiously enough, the diameters of the clusters seem to increase progressively with increasing distance from the earth.

Now a systematic effect of this sort requires explanation. We can scarcely believe that the earth is so important that the clusters are arranged symmetrically in relation to it. It seems more probable that the progression in size can be traced to some peculiarity of the observations or calculations. In measuring the distances it is assumed that the intervening spaces are perfectly transparent. Suppose they are filled with a tenuous fog. Then the distant cluster viewed through this medium appears fainter, and therefore seems to be more distant than it really is. To fill the angle that it does, the size of the cluster must come out too large also; and the amount of this overestimate must grow larger as the cluster is more distant.

To explain the progressive increase in the measured diameters of the open clusters Trumpler supposes that there is a layer of absorbing stuff a few hundred light-years thick, lying along the plane of the Milky Way.

A star at the distance of three thousand light-years, observed entirely through this absorbing layer, is reduced in brightness fifty per cent. A stratum of this sort has not much effect on the celestial bodies whose positions in the sky are far from the Milky Way. The open clusters which congregate toward this plane are conspicuously affected. So also must the star clouds which form the Milky Way be affected. Viewed through this foggy medium they must appear fainter and therefore seem to be much farther away than they really are. The whole Milky Way system shrinks from the usually accepted diameter of around two hundred thousand light-years to a diameter of only thirty or forty thousand light-years. Such is Trumpler's conclusion based on his studies of the open clusters, a conclusion which must be carefully investigated.

GLOBULAR CLUSTERS

The second category of star clusters comprises the larger and more spectacular globular clusters. These great balls of stars avoid the congested regions of the Milky Way proper; they are located in the outskirts of our system, where the stellar population is otherwise scanty. Ninety-three are known in this system. Ten have been discovered in the Magellanic Clouds.

The nearest and brightest of the globular clusters are Omega Centauri and 47 Tucanæ, neither of which is well placed for observers in the United States. At the distance of 22,000 light-years, they appear as hazy stars of the fourth magnitude, so that they are plainly visible to the unaided eye. The telescope shows them as globes of stars, slightly flattened globes, to be sure, showing that they are rotating and are flattened at the poles, like the earth. Photographs with long exposures bring out their stars by the thousands, though the congestion near the center is too great for reliable counts.

Messier 13, the great cluster in Hercules, is the finest globular cluster for observers with the telescope in middle northern latitudes. It passes nearly overhead in the early evening during the late summer. Those who recognize the constellation Hercules by the figure of a butterfly can find the location of the cluster two thirds of the way from the head to the tip of the northern wing. At best, it is only faintly visible to the naked eye. But with the telescope, and especially on the photographs, it is a truly remarkable sight.

At the distance of 34,000 light-years, only the brighter stars of the cluster can be seen. A star no more luminous than our sun could not be detected with the largest telescope. Fifty thousand stars are visible—more than twenty times as many as the eye alone can see in the whole sky at any one time. The whole membership of the Hercules cluster must number hundreds of thousands of stars. The densest part has a diameter of thirty light-years. Most of the stars in the cluster are within a region sixty or seventy light-years across. The number of stars is considerably greater than in an equal volume of space around the sun. If we lived near the center of this cluster we should have a more brilliant array of constellations in our sky than the one with which we are familiar.

Shapley's studies of the globular clusters, at Mount

Wilson and Harvard, have given reliable information
of their distances, which range from 22,000 to 185,-
000 light-years. The clusters avoid the central plane
of the Milky Way, but they are symmetrically distributed on either side of it, showing that they are
associated with the system of its star clouds. The
globular clusters are distributed over a region of space
more than 200,000 light-years in diameter, whose
center is 50,000 light-years distant from the earth in
the direction of the constellation Sagittarius. If we
suppose that the clusters outline the system of the
Milky Way, the *galactic system*, then the diameter of
this great system of ours is 200,000 light-years, or
somewhat less, and its center is 50,000 light-years
away in the direction of Sagittarius.

STAR CLOUDS OF THE MILKY WAY

The finest part of the Milky Way for observers in
middle northern latitudes is the part we see in the early
evening in the late summer and autumn. It stretches
across the heavens from northeast to southwest, as a
broad luminous band. On a clear moonless night and
in the absence of artificial lights it is one of the most
impressive of all spectacles that are revealed to the
naked eye.

We follow its course upward from the northeast
horizon through Perseus, Cassiopeia's Chair, and
Cepheus to the region of the Northern Cross, near
the zenith in the early evening at the beginning of
autumn. Here the Milky Way divides into two parallel
streams, and remains so divided nearly as far as the

FIG. 45.—*The Globular Cluster in Hercules.* (*From a photograph at the Mount Wilson Observatory.*)

Southern Cross. This great rift and the many smaller ones, as we shall notice more particularly in the following chapter, are not breaks in the Milky Way, but dark cosmic dust clouds which hide the stars beyond.

Southward from Cygnus the western branch fades and then becomes brighter again before it crosses the horizon. The eastern branch grows brighter through Aquila, and south of this constellation gathers into the spectacular Scutum and Sagittarius star clouds. This, with the neighboring regions of Ophiuchus and Scorpio, is easily the most remarkable part of the Milky Way, whether we observe with the unaided eye or with the telescope. Photographs with telescopes of short focus bring out the details clearly. Barnard's photographs of this and other parts of the Milky Way visible in middle northern latitudes are easily among the finest. These he made with the 10-inch Bruce telescope, partly on Mount Wilson, the remainder at the Yerkes Observatory.

Below the south horizon the Milky Way passes through Centaurus, where the rift ends, and through the fine region of the Southern Cross, where it is nearest the south pole of the heavens. Turning northward again, it comes into our view as a single broad stream in the winter skies. This part of the Milky Way is less brilliant than the part we see in summer, and it does not gather so conspicuously into star clouds. We follow it in the early evening in midwinter past the Dog Stars and Orion, through Gemini and Auriga, near the zenith, into Perseus again.

In the Milky Way we view the star clouds of our galactic system projected around a circle of the heavens. Evidently the circle which passes centrally along this luminous girdle marks the principal plane of this flat system. Our problem is to construct a picture of the system itself from the projected view. In the closing chapter we shall notice that progress is being made on this picture, and that astronomers are venturing far beyond the confines of this system in the discovery and study of the external galaxies.

Nebulæ, both bright and dark, have an important rôle in the construction of the galaxies. The attention is drawn, first of all, to the nebulæ in our galactic system.

V

THE NEBULÆ

IN FORMER times, all faintly luminous patches in the heavens, except the star clouds of the Milky Way, were known as "nebulæ," that is to say, "clouds." A few of these objects are visible to the naked eye. Multitudes are brought into view with the telescope. The Herschels discovered, catalogued, and described large numbers of them.

Some nebulæ are known by special names, such as the Great Nebula in Orion, the North America Nebula, and the Trifid Nebula. The brighter ones are often designated by their running numbers in the catalogue of 103 nebulæ which Messier, famous as the discoverer of many comets, prepared a century and a half ago. These objects can easily be mistaken for comets by the observer with a small telescope. Messier 31, for example, is the Great Nebula in Andromeda. But in general, nebulæ are now designated by number as they appear in Dreyer's *New General Catalogue*, which, with its two extensions, lists thirteen thousand nebulæ and star clusters. The Andromeda nebula is N. G. C. 223.

The opinions of earlier astronomers concerning the nature of the nebulæ differed widely. Kant's conjecture that they are very remote galaxies of stars—"island universes"—gained a considerable following. William Herschel reached the conclusion that some of them are not of a starry nature, but are instead composed of a luminous fluid. Laplace's famous nebular hypothesis traces the development of the sun and its planetary system by the contraction of a mass of gaseous nebula. But the idea that the nebulæ are gaseous seemed to be contradicted as telescopes increased in size. More and more nebulæ were resolved into stars. Toward the middle of the nineteenth century, the Earl of Rosse's great six-foot reflecting telescope, the largest in the world at that time and for many years to follow, was very effective in revealing nebulæ so-called as simply distant clusters of stars.

But all nebulæ are not clusters of stars. William Huggins, in England, pioneer in the use of the spectroscope in astronomy, definitely established the truth of Herschel's conjecture that some nebulæ are composed of a "shining fluid." In 1864, Huggins directed his spectroscope toward a nebula in Draco, and viewed a pattern of bright lines—the spectrum of a glowing gas. It was now evident that some of the nebulæ are gaseous. Others, however, gave patterns of dark lines resembling the spectra of stars, although they showed no indication of being resolved into star clusters. The nebulæ still presented mysteries to be solved.

All star clusters in our galactic system are now clearly distinguished from nebulæ. Moreover, researches of very recent years have shown that many objects formerly classed as nebulæ are in reality remote galaxies far beyond our Milky Way. Their descriptions are reserved for the following chapter.

The nebulæ proper, which are found in our galactic system and in the external galaxies also, are divided generally into two classes: diffuse nebulæ, both bright and dark, and planetary nebulæ.

BRIGHT DIFFUSE NEBULÆ

The great nebula in Orion (Figure 46) is the most famous of the bright diffuse nebulæ. To the naked eye it appears as the middle star of the three that mark Orion's sword, a little way south of the brighter three in his belt. Examined with the telescope, it appears as a roughly triangular mass of faintly luminous material. Apparently, the distance across the nebula is twice the diameter of the full moon. Actually, it is ten light-years across—an enormous cloud. Photographs with wide-angle lenses and long exposures show fainter nebulosity spreading over the greater part of the entire constellation of Orion.

The Trifid Nebula in Sagittarius is another fine example of bright diffuse nebulosity. At first sight one might imagine that it is breaking into three or more pieces, for wide, dark rifts run across it. They are in reality streaks of dark nebulosity which is often found associated with the luminous material. The brightest stars of the Pleiades are involved in nebulosities which add greatly to the interest of this cluster on the photographs, though the eye at the telescope sees ordinarily only the stars. It frequently happens that striking nebulæ on the photographs cannot be discerned at all visually even with the largest telescopes.

This is true of the North America Nebula, so named

by Wolf of Heidelberg because of its resemblance to the continent. Located in the Milky Way near the bright star in Cygnus which marks the top of the Northern Cross, it is a remarkable object on the photographs. In the same constellation there is a great oval loop of nebulosity which appears to be expanding. The suggestion is advanced that it may have resulted from the explosion of a star. If this is the correct explanation, and if the rate of expansion has remained the same, the mighty outburst of the new star must have occurred more than a hundred thousand years ago. The brightest parts of the loop are known as the Network Nebula and the Filamentary Nebula, both of intricate structure, as their names imply.

These are examples of bright diffuse nebulæ which the telescope and especially the photographs show in considerable numbers. They are found in or near the Milky Way and in the external galaxies as well. In fact, the largest known nebula of this kind lies outside the Milky Way system proper; it is in the Large Magellanic Cloud. The diameter of this nebula, which is known as 30 Doradus, is more than a hundred light-years.

Diffuse nebulæ are enormous clouds of gas and fine dust. In many ways they remind us of the filmy tails of comets. Their material is so greatly dispersed that it is much less dense than the best vacuum obtained in the laboratory. It is only the great thickness of nebulæ that makes them visible at all. And their light is as feeble as it seems to be in the distance. If we lived within the North America Nebula, we would be unaware ordinarily of its existence.

THE LIGHT OF THE NEBULÆ

What causes these nebulæ to be luminous? Certainly, such highly attenuated material cannot be hot enough to shine. The answer to this problem which puzzled astronomers for many years was clearly stated by Hubble, not long ago, as a result of his extensive studies of nebulæ with the great reflecting telescopes on Mount Wilson. Nebulæ are made luminous by neighboring stars. For almost every one a near-by or actually involved star, or stars, can be held responsible for the illumination. And more than this, the brighter the associated star, the greater the distance to which the nebular glow extends around the star. But the light of nebulæ is not simply reflected starlight; at least, it can scarcely be the case for all nebulæ.

Spectroscopic investigations bring out an interesting relation between the light of the nebula and of the associated star. In the neighborhood of all except the hottest stars, the nebular light resembles the starlight. Both show the same dark line spectrum, the same pattern of dark lines. The nebulosities surrounding the Pleiades are examples of such similarity. On the other hand, the great nebula in Orion and many others which are associated with the hottest stars shine with a different light. Their spectra are patterns of bright lines, unlike the stellar spectra. What conclusions can we draw from these relations?

Concerning the first class, astronomers are not in complete agreement. Some believe that these nebulæ shine simply by reflected starlight. But the light of the bright-line nebulæ is clearly not starlight. Yet the associated stars are responsible for the illumination. We are reminded of the auroral glow in the earth's atmosphere, which is not reflected sunlight. The light of comets presents a similar problem. We conclude that the Orion nebula and others like it are illuminated with a sort of auroral glow, analogous to our "northern lights," owing to the influence of hot stars near by.

For many years, scientists were puzzled by the bright lines in the spectra of nebulæ. Some of the lines, to be sure, were definitely identified with the well known elements hydrogen and helium. There was nothing mysterious about them. But certain other bright lines in the nebular spectra had never been seen in the laboratory. Could it be possible that the nebulæ contained a chemical element not found on the earth? Provisionally, the name "nebulium" was assigned to this element, just as helium was named for the sun, because it was discovered in the solar spectrum before it was identified on the earth. "Nebulium," however, is not an element. The puzzling bright lines in the spectra of the nebulæ are produced by the common elements oxygen and nitrogen under the unusual conditions which prevail there, conditions which are impossible to duplicate in the laboratory. Thus the problem of the strange lines is solved.

PLANETARY NEBULÆ

Planetary nebulæ have nothing in common with the planets. The name arises from the fact that they appear in the telescope as elliptical disks. They are considerably flattened globes of nebulous material, enor-

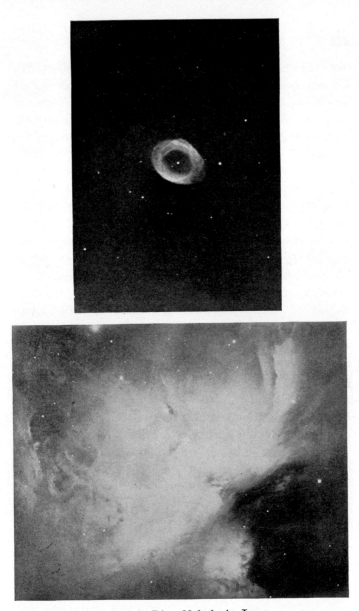

Fig. 46.—(above) *Ring Nebula in Lyra.*
(below) *Great Nebula in Orion.* (*From
photographs at Mount Wilson Observatory.*)

mously larger than planets, much larger even than the whole solar system. The flattening is owing to their rotation, which the spectroscope proves independently. Some, it is true, present practically circular disks; evidently these have their axes directed nearly toward the earth. The periods of rotation are expressed in thousands of years.

More than a hundred planetary nebulæ are known. Probably they are all about the same size; their difference in apparent size is owing to their difference in distance. The helical nebulæ N. G. C. 7293, in Aquarius, which is probably the nearest of the planetaries, appears more than a third as large as the full moon. The most distant ones can scarcely be distinguished from stars with the telescope, although they are easily identified with the spectroscope.

Differences of brightness over the disks of planetary nebulæ give them individuality. The "Owl Nebula," in Ursa Major, one of the nearest and therefore one of the largest with the telescope, is so named because of two dark spots which may be imagined to resemble the eyes of the owl. The "Dumbbell Nebula," in Vulpecula, is darkened around the ends of the long axis of its elliptical disk—a rather common occurrence—so that it appears as a dumbbell. One of the planetaries bears some resemblance to the planet Saturn with its rings nearly edgewise. Others exhibit concentric rings. Still others have the appearance of thick rings, the central part of the disk being darkened.

The Ring Nebula, in Lyra (Figure 46), is the finest of the planetary nebulæ as viewed with a telescope of moderate size. Situated in the southern part of the constellation Lyra, between the eclipsing star Beta and its neighbor, Gamma, it is invisible to the naked eye and with small telescopes. With larger instruments it has the appearance of a somewhat flattened luminous doughnut. On the photographs complex structural details appear in the ring, and a star is shown at its center. The central star, an unusually blue star, is characteristic of the planetary nebulæ, almost without exception; it is evidently the source of their illumination.

Concerning the relation of the planetary nebulæ to other celestial objects we have no definite information as yet. It might be imagined that they have something in common with novæ, or temporary stars. Novæ, like the planetaries, are strongly concentrated toward the Milky Way. In their later stages they are not unlike the central stars of the planetaries, and gaseous envelopes are observed around some of the novæ. Around Nova Aquilæ, which burst out in 1918, a nebulous shell has been expanding at the rate of fifty million miles a day.

DARK NEBULÆ

Nebulæ are made luminous, as we have seen, by stars in their vicinities. In the absence of such stars they remain dark and are revealed to us only as they obstruct in places the view of the bright celestial scenery beyond. Like the bright nebulæ in our galactic system, these dark dust clouds are strongly concentrated toward the Milky Way. It is a fortunate arrangement, because they can be seen clearly against this luminous band of the sky.

The most conspicuous of the "vacant places" in the Milky Way is the great dark rift which extends from the region of the Northern Cross nearly to the Southern Cross, dividing the Milky Way into two parallel starry streams over a third of its entire course around the heavens. North of the Northern Cross a transverse rift is easily seen. Near the Southern Cross there is a dark patch nearly as large as the Cross itself, in which very few stars can be seen. This remarkable "hole" in the midst of the brilliant star clouds has long been known as the "Coal Sack," the name given it by the early mariners.

Until very recent times the dark rifts in the Milky Way were regarded generally as openings through which we look into dark space beyond. This explanation, to be sure, was not altogether satisfactory. If the star clouds have considerable thickness, the openings were tunnels. Why they should be directed toward the earth was not easy to explain. Nor was it obvious how the tunnels could remain open for any length of time, since the multitudes of stars around them are in motion in various directions. Barnard at the Yerkes Observatory was among the first to view the rifts as intervening dark dust clouds.

To appreciate fully the great number and varied forms of the dark nebulæ one has only to examine the excellent photographs of the Milky Way which are now available. All along its course this luminous stream is marked up in a bewildering way. This is especially true in the region of Ophiuchus where some of the most surprising forms are exhibited. The majority of the obscuring clouds are in our local system of stars, only a few thousand light-years distant from the earth. They are present in the external galaxies also, as we notice in the following chapter.

Dark nebulæ, like the bright ones, are great clouds of gas and dust. It is not improbable that they contain larger solid pieces as well. Comets and meteor swarms have similar constitution. Indeed, it has been suggested that those which are now revolving around the sun were picked up several million years ago when our solar system passed through one of the dark clouds.

NEBULAR HYPOTHESES

In former times, when theories of cosmic evolution were taken somewhat more seriously than they are at present, nebulæ were believed to represent the most primitive state of material in the universe. How the nebulæ came to be was not understood. They stood for primeval chaos, out of which orderly arrays of stars and planets developed. Nearly two centuries ago, the philosopher Kant proposed the first of the nebular hypotheses. He chose the nebula as the initial stage, because it seemed to him the simplest form that could follow nothing at all. The course of evolution seemed to him naturally to proceed from the simple to the complex, a point of view that was followed generally in subsequent theories. Laplace's account of cosmic evolution which is known as "the nebular hypotheses," and in which the development of the solar system is specially treated, is the most famous of all.

Until recent times it was generally supposed that the stars have developed by contraction from the bright nebulæ, such as the great nebula in Orion. And the stars of different colors were believed to be stars of different ages. Young stars were the hottest and therefore the bluest. As they cooled and contracted, they became in middle age yellow stars like the sun. Still cooler in old age, they reddened. Gradually their light became redder and feebler until they ceased to shine. This classical theory was not complete in all respects. It was not understood how the hottest star could follow as the next stage after the cold nebula. Yet the close association of blue stars with bright nebulæ seemed to establish their extreme youth. The blue stars of the Pleiades, for example, are involved in nebulosity. But this association, as we have seen, has now a different significance. The nebulæ become luminous only when there are hot stars near by.

The original theory of stellar evolution was of a one-way process, from tenuous nebulæ to dense, dark stars. But in 1913, Russell showed that the sequence from blue stars to red stars forms two branches. One branch comprises giant and supergiant stars, larger and more luminous than the sun; and of these the red stars are the largest and least dense. The second branch comprises smaller stars of the "main sequence," including the sun, which become smaller and denser with increasing redness. To interpret the new data, a different theory of stellar development was proposed and widely adopted for the following decade. The stars are formed by the contraction of dark nebulæ. At first they are great red stars, cool and not very bright per square foot of surface; yet their enormous size places them among the most luminous stars. With increasing age these stars shrink. For a time they develop more heat by contraction than they radiate. They become hotter, changing from red to yellow and then to blue. At this point the contraction is less rapid. Less heat is gained thereby than is radiated. The star cools, changing in color from blue to yellow and then to red. Finally it ceases to shine.

Both theories begin with nebulæ and end with dark stars. In both of them, contraction is the outstanding feature. Examining them, we wonder whether a time will come when there are no more nebulæ and all the stars have faded to invisibility. But we recall that these are pioneer theories concerning a very difficult subject. Processes of cosmic development are exceedingly slow and therefore hard to trace. We have no certain evidence that stars are progressively contracting.

We turn now from these conjectures as to remote past and future of the universe to survey it as it appears to-day. The stars and nebulæ are assembled in enormous galaxies which claim our attention.

VI
GALAXIES

In the description of the Milky Way we have noticed some of the star clouds, in particular, the great Sagittarius cloud whose center is 50,000 light-years away, and the somewhat smaller and nearer Scutum cloud. According to the view recently set forth by Shapley, these and other star clouds are *galaxies*, that is to say, vast assemblages of stars and nebulæ. They average 10,000 light-years in diameter. Some are considerably smaller, while the largest are three or four times greater in diameter.

The galaxy of which our sun is a member is known as the *local system*. It is a considerably flattened assemblage of about average size, containing the lucid stars which form our constellations, the majority of the millions of stars visible in telescopes of moderate size, many of the open star clusters, and practically all of the bright and dark nebulæ which congregate along the Milky Way. Viewed from another part of the Milky Way system, our local system would appear as one of the star clouds. In the local system the sun has a fairly central position; the center is three hundred light-years away in the direction of the southern constellation Carina.

These star clouds are grouped nearly in one plane in the supergalaxy which we call the galactic system.

For the past century and a half, astronomers have been trying to determine precisely the form and extent of this system whose principal feature, as we see it in projection on our skies, is the Milky Way. The problem has been a difficult one, owing to our position within the system; it would be greatly simplified if we could obtain a view from the outside. The difficulty has been increased by the lack, until very recently, of any means of determining the distances of celestial objects more remote than those immediately around us in the local system.

Two ways of studying the structure of the galactic system have been employed chiefly. The first is by counting stars in equal areas in many different parts of the sky; the counts provide data for a statistical study. This method was first employed by Sir William Herschel, who counted the number of stars visible in the field of his telescope in each of more than three thousand regions of the sky. On the assumption that a greater number of stars in any direction meant their greater extension in that direction, Herschel concluded that the galactic system has the form of a grindstone having its axis at right angles to the plane of the Milky Way and a diameter of six thousand light-years, according to the scale of distance now available. Herschel's system was too small, because his 19-inch reflector could show him only the nearer stars. It was the first systematic attempt to survey the galactic system. This statistical method has since been employed many times, with improvements in telescopic power and in methods. The counts are now made on photographs of representative regions of the sky. The most recent results were announced in 1928, by Seares at the Mount Wilson Observatory.

The second method of studying the structure of the galactic system is to determine the distances of objects in many places throughout the system. Evidently, if we have the directions and distances of many features of the system, we can make a model representing its form and dimensions. As we have seen, the distance of a Cepheid variable star can be determined wherever a Cepheid is found; and these useful stars are scattered throughout the galactic system. By means of Cepheids, and in other ways which astronomers have devised in recent years, the survey of the galactic system is now proceeding rapidly, at the Harvard Observatory and elsewhere. In the course of a dozen years we shall have more nearly complete information concerning the form and extent of the galactic system. Meanwhile there is considerable difference of opinion.

There is at present, as we noticed in an earlier chapter, a reliable model of the system of globular clusters. These clusters are arranged symmetrically with respect to the plane of the Milky Way around a region of space 200,000 light-years or more in diameter. If we suppose that the globular clusters outline the galactic system, then this system has a diameter of 200,000 light-years; and its center is the center cf the cluster system. The center lies in the direction of the great Sagittarius star cloud.

At first, many astronomers assumed that the entire system of the Milky Way is a single galaxy. And since many of the external galaxies are spirals, it was easy to imagine that ours has the spiral form. On this assumption, the Sagittarius cloud is the massive nucleus from which the spiral arms emerge; our local system is a smaller assemblage in one of the arms, about half-way from the center to the edge.

Recent observations seem to show that the galactic system is in rotation, as the distant spirals are known to be. As our share in this rotation, we are moving at the rate of two hundred miles a second, at present in the direction of the constellation Cepheus. This evidence might be taken as supporting the view that the galactic system is a single spiral galaxy. If so, it is by far the largest known galaxy, five times greater in diameter than the largest of the others. This discrepancy is embarrassing.

The view proposed by Shapley in 1930 is somewhat different. The galactic system is a supergalaxy in which the star clouds are the separate galaxies. The whole system is not a spiral, but some of the galaxies may be. This is the view that we adopt provisionally. The local galaxy immediately around us and the other galaxies of the Milky Way system have dimensions comparable among themselves and with the external galaxies. This agreement recommends the theory. But our supergalaxy, only a fifth of a million light-years across, is smaller than the remote supergalaxies. This discrepancy will disappear, however, if some of the neighboring galaxies which are not in the plane of the Milky Way are found to be members, nevertheless, of our supergalaxy.

The two Magellanic Clouds are nearer than many of the globular clusters, although they are far from the Milky Way. Near the south pole of the heavens, they never appear above the horizon in middle northern latitudes. The Large Cloud, at the distance of 86,000 light-years, is a little more than 10,000 light-years in diameter. The Small Cloud lies slightly farther away, at the distance of 95,000 light-years; its diameter is 6,000 light-years. Both are plainly visible to the naked eye as cloudy patches in the sky. With the telescope they are found to contain stars, star clusters, nebulæ, and other familiar features of the local system around us. In size as well they resemble the star clouds of the Milky Way. If they were in its plane, there would be nothing to distinguish the Magellanic Clouds from the other star clouds. Their motions also are such as to suggest that they are members of the supergalaxy to which our galactic system belongs.

A quarter of a century before Herschel began his celebrated explorations of the heavens, Thomas Wright, of Durham, England, set forth the theory that the system of the stars has the form of a flat circular disk. The philosopher, Kant, in 1755, went still further. He conjectured that the nebulæ are remote milky ways far beyond our own—"island universes," they have been called in accordance with this view. But at that time, and indeed until very recent years, there was no known way of determining the distances of these objects, and so of proving or discrediting this speculation.

The hazy objects originally designated as nebulæ, excluding those that have proved to be star clusters, fall sharply into two groups. The first group crowd toward the Milky Way; these are the "galactic nebulæ," or nebulæ proper, which were described in the previous chapter. The second group are found in all parts of the heavens, except in the vicinity of the Milky Way, where they are hidden behind the dark clouds and other absorbing material along the galactic plane. These, which include the spiral nebulæ, came to be known as extra-galactic nebulæ. And within the past twenty years there was a movement to revive the "island universe" theory with the extra-galactic nebulæ as the "islands." But the movement made little progress as long as the distances of these objects remained unknown.

Definite knowledge of galaxies far beyond the Milky Way was inaugurated by Shapley at Harvard, in 1923. He showed that the distant star cloud which is known to astronomers as N. G. C. 6822 is much more remote than any part of the Milky Way system. The existence of one "island universe" at least was clearly established. This galaxy, whose distance is 625,000 light-years, resembles the Magellanic Clouds.

Hubble's success in photographing individual stars in some of the nearest spirals was the next step. Cepheid variable stars are among the stars shown on his photographs of these spirals with the 100-inch Mount Wilson telescope. Their distances, and therefore the distances of the spirals in which they were found, could now be determined. It was necessary only to photograph these spirals often enough to establish the periods of their Cepheid variables. By this procedure Hubble demonstrated, in 1925, that the spiral nebulæ are galaxies far beyond the Milky Way.

The "Great Nebula in Andromeda" is the brightest of the spirals, and the only one clearly visible to the

FIG. 47.—*Great Spiral in Andromeda. (From a photograph at Yerkes Observatory.)*

naked eye. It is easily found in the evening skies of the fall and winter by anyone who is familiar with the Square of Pegasus. Imagine that this square is the bowl of a dipper, and find its handle extending toward the northeast. A little way northwest of the second star in the handle, the great spiral appears to the naked eye as an elongated, faintly luminous patch in the sky. The structure is not revealed by the telescope, but is clearly brought out in the photographs. It is a flat spiral inclined 15° from the edgewise position (Figure 47). The bright nucleus, which is visible to the unaided eye, is surrounded by the fainter coils. The distance of the Andromeda spiral is 800,000 light-years. It is a giant among the galaxies.

In the neighboring constellation Triangulum, the nearest of the spirals, Messier 33, can be scarcely discerned with the naked eye. Although it is about five per cent nearer than the Andromeda spiral, this galaxy is smaller and therefore fainter; its diameter is 15,000 light-years. The Triangulum spiral is more nearly flatwise, so that its structure is exhibited clearly. The arms emerge from opposite sides of the nucleus, and coil in the same sense and in the same plane.

Two million external galaxies, it is estimated, are bright enough to be visible with the 100-inch telescope; and the majority are spirals. Their distances range from less than a million to 150 million light-years. The spirals average from five to ten thousand light-years in diameter, depending on how closely they are coiled. They are presented to us in various ways, from the flatwise view such as we have of the familiar "Whirlpool Nebula" in Canes Venatici, near the Great Dipper, to the edgewise position.

Turned edgewise to the earth, the spirals appear like spindles. Characteristic of this view is a dark band extending lengthwise along the spindle, and in some cases seeming to cut it in two. The appearance of the dark equatorial band in these spirals reminds us of the dark dust clouds in our own galaxy, and especially of the long dark rift in the Milky Way. Examined with the spectroscope, the spirals that are presented edgewise, or nearly so, are found to be in rotation, as we might well suppose from their flattened form. The nucleus of the Andromeda spiral has a period of rotation of about 16 million years.

Not all external galaxies have the spiral form. There is a small percentage of galaxies resembling the Magellanic Clouds. There are also "elliptical nebulæ" which have not been resolved into stars. Their disks range from nearly circles to much-flattened ellipses; and in the flattest ones the ends of the long axis are drawn out so that they have the appearance of double convex lenses presented edgewise to us.

The galaxies, like individual stars, are assembled in clusters which are known as supergalaxies. As many as forty supergalaxies are already listed, varying in membership from a few to hundreds of galaxies. Several fine examples appear in the vicinity of the constellation Virgo. A great supergalaxy in Centaurus, recently studied at the Harvard Observatory, contains some giant galaxies comparable with the Andromeda spiral. A group of galaxies in Pegasus has been likened to our galactic system.

In the few years that have elapsed since the recognition of the external galaxies, much has been learned about them. Much remains to be learned. Practically all the problems which the stars have presented arise again with respect to the galaxies. Just as the stars around us are assembled in a galaxy, we may suppose that the galaxies and supergalaxies are members of a greater organization, the metagalaxy, whose form and extent must remain unknown until telescopes are constructed powerful enough to reach to its boundaries. And what lies beyond? Other metagalaxies? And do these form a system still more vast? We can for the present only speculate on these questions.

Among the remarkable disclosures of recent years concerning the external galaxies, none is more surprising than the rapidity with which they seem to be withdrawing from us. This evidence is derived from the study of their spectra, by observing the displacements of the spectral lines. With allowance for the effect of our own motion, the external galaxies are receding from us at enormous rates which are progressively greater for more distant galaxies. The Mount Wilson astronomers announce that a faint galaxy in Ursa Major is speeding away from us at the rate of more than 7,000 miles a second. When more distant galaxies can be observed with the spectroscope, they will doubtless exhibit still faster motions of recession.

Some years ago, Einstein concluded that space would be boundless if it contained no matter. Since it contains matter, space is bounded; and the more material there is in the universe, the shorter is the radius of space. Some scientists are now of the opinion that the amount of matter in the universe is steadily decreasing. They suppose that the masses of the stars are diminishing in order to keep up their radiations. If this is true, then two and a half million tons of the sun alone is being transformed into sunshine every second. With loss of material, space expands, according to the view we have mentioned. Lemaître, in Belgium, has developed mathematical formulæ to describe an expanding universe. In a construction of this sort distant objects must be receding from us very rapidly, as the external galaxies are observed to do.